English Result

Elementary Workbook Answer Key Booklet

Joe McKenna

OXFORD

Unit 1

1

1A

1
a 3
b 1
c 2

2
1 Hello
2 What's your name
3 What's your name again
4 My name's
5 Oops
6 And you

3
1 Hello again, Julia!
2 Hello, Bob! My name's Jennifer!
3 Oops! Hello, Jennifer. How are you?
4 I'm fine thanks. And you?
5 I'm fine too.

4 Jane; Drew

5
1 Jane
2 Drew
3 Drew

1B

1
1 384 6652
   499 7411
   406 5889
   221 3075

2 iou20@busby.net
   okchen@vanzine.int
   quick4@spt.com
   lin3@lovebird.org

3 www.boptunes.esl
   www.ugetwell.co.uk
   www.digipix.net
   www.readit.net

2 Good morning! How are you?

4
1 your; My
2 her; her
3 his; his

1C

1
1 22
2 37
3 44
4 70
5 118
6 65
7 53
8 89
9 96
10 101

2 Across
2 eighty-two
5 seventy-six
7 thirty-one
8 fifty
9 forty

Down
1 forty-nine
3 twenty-two
4 thirty-three
6 ninety-four

3
1 I'm
2 he's
3 she's
4 we're
5 they're

4
1 I'm; My
2 She's; Her
3 He's; His
4 We're; Our
5 They're; Their

5
1 c
2 d
3 a
4 e
5 b

1D

1
1 Excuse me; please; Thank you
2 thanks
3 sorry
4 Sorry; Thanks
5 Excuse me

2
1 We're; We're
2 is; She's
3 I'm; I'm
4 It's; Is; He's
5 are; They're
6 is; isn't; she's

3
1 d
2 c
3 f
4 a
5 b
6 e

4
a 1
b 6
c 3
d 2
e 5
f 4

Skills Practice

1 Ivana Kuznetsov
Russia
667 4321
kuznetsov@len.ac.ru

Brian J. Wilson
Canada
0909 8790981
bjwilson@pqoil.net

Yvonne Chanut
France
01632 960 0120
yvchan@servling.net

Enrique Delgado
Spain
0191 498 0996
edelgado17@spc.net

3
1 **Surname** Raharjo
   Age 35
   Country Holland
   Email marwara@belanda.net

2 **First name** Gillian
   Marital status single
   Phone 976 343 918
   ID no. SA 500255

3 **First name** Sean
   Age 31
   Marital status married
   ID no. RI 2273168

4
1 2
2 3
3 1
4 3
5 2
6 3

6
1 He's 35.
2 ✓
3 It's 623 579210.
4 She's single.
5 ✓
6 It's gilvdp@saturnus.net.
7 His surname is Collins.
8 It's RI 227 3168.
9 He is married.
10 ✓

9
1 The letter is from Gillian.
2 Gillian is in Scotland.
3 Johann and Sandra are married.
4 Johann is from Germany.
5 Gillian is in a café.
6 There isn't a telephone in her room./There is no telephone in her room.
7 Sandra's mobile number is 07700 900 787.
8 There are computers in the hotel.

10
1 Mr S. Collins
2 4 Cathedral St.
3 Cork
4 Ireland

Unit 2

2A

1
1 pencil
2 picture
3 umbrella
4 window
5 student
6 map
7 desk
8 chair
9 teacher
10 board

2
1 What's this in English?
2 Can you repeat that, please?
3 How do you spell that?
4 Can you say that slowly, please?
5 Can you write that, please?

3
1 open
2 ask
3 write
4 close
5 listen
6 look
7 read

4 **2 syllables**   question, Monday,
Wednesday, answer,
evening, English, weekend,
Thursday,
3 syllables   afternoon, underline,
umbrella, Saturday

2B

1
1 Luca is Mark's son.
2 Luca is Caitlin's brother.
3 Caroline is Mark's wife.
4 Mark is Luca's father.
5 ✓
6 Luca is Caroline's son.
7 ✓
8 Caitlin is Mark's daughter.
9 Caitlin and Luca are Mark and
Caroline's children.

2
1 **His** wife**'s** name**'s** Caroline.
2 **His** sister**'s** name**'s** Caitlin.
3 **Her** children**'s** names **are** Caitlin
and Luca.
4 **Her** father**'s** name**'s** Mark.
5 They**'re** Caitlin and Luca**'s** parents.
6 They**'re** Mark and Caroline**'s**
children.

3
1 That's my dog.
2 Those are my sons.
3 These are my parents.
4 This is my daughter.
5 That's my husband.

2C

1
1 grandfather
2 grandmother
3 boyfriend
4 girlfriend
5 married couple
6 farmer
7 taxi driver
8 office worker
9 factory worker
10 footballer
11 model
12 artist
13 singer

2
1 a
2 a
3 a
4 an
5 a
6 a
7 an

3
1 a university student
2 a doctor
3 a married couple
4 an engineer
5 a school teacher
6 a young boy
7 an office worker

4
1 a young woman
2 married
3 a retired engineer
4 a taxi driver
5 a divorced couple
6 a shop assistant
7 rich

5
1 His girlfriend‿is‿an‿English teacher.
2 Her parents‿are designers.
3 She's‿an‿engineer.
4 The shop‿assistant‿is sixteen
years‿old.
5 My boyfriend‿is‿a good‿actor.

2D

1
1 a
2 a
3 b
4 b
5 b
6 b

2
1 False
2 True
3 False
4 False
5 True
6 False
7 True
8 True

3
1 on; at
2 on; at
3 at; on
4 at; on
5 on; at
6 at; on
7 on; at

4
1 TV2
2 Monday evening
3 Monday morning
4 twelve o'clock
5 twenty past eight
6 five to ten
7 the football

Skills Practice

1
a 2
b 4
c 3
d 1

2

Doctor	Tuesday, Thursday	6.00–9.00
Office	Tuesday to Friday	9.30–2.30
Shop	Monday to Saturday	9.00–4.30
School	Monday to Friday	8.30–4.30

3 Doctor Watson's office **is closed at**
the moment. The doctor is available
on Tuesday **and Thursday evenings**,
from …

5
a 5
b 1
c 2
d 4
e 3

6
1 d, b
2 g, a
3 i, f
4 j, c
5 h, e

8
1 d (look at the pictures in the book)
2 f (repeat the words together)
3 c (listen to conversations on the CD)
4 b (have a conversation with our
partner)
5 e (read texts from the book)
6 g (write answers)
7 a (ask the teacher questions)

9
1 b
2 c
3 d
4 a

10
1 she's single
2 she has a daughter
3 her name is Janaina
4 they have two children

11 This is Stella McCartney. She's an
English designer. Her father is a singer.
She's 33 years old and she's married.
Her husband's name is Alasdhair. They
have a baby son.

Unit 3

3A

1

platform	pub
cash machine	exit
bookshop	ticket office
toilets	train
station	restaurant
chemist's	bus
car park	taxi

2
1 platform
2 ticket office
3 restaurant
4 bookshop
5 car park
6 pub

3
1 Where are the toilets, please?
2 I think they're upstairs.
3 Is platform 5 near here?
4 This is platform 5!
5 Is this the bus to Manchester?
6 Where's the café?

4
1 Manchester; platform
2 telephones; exit
3 café; music shop
4 car park; chemist's
5 cash machines; bookshop

5
- •• platform, exit, café, car park, chemist's, bookshop
- ••• Manchester, telephones, music shop, cash machines

3B

1
1 d
2 e
3 h
4 b
5 f
6 c
7 g
8 i
9 a

2
-n	Indian, South African
-ian	Canadian, Peruvian, Brazilian
-ish	Spanish, Turkish
-ese	Japanese, Chinese

3
1 d
2 c
3 a
4 e
5 b

4
1 the
2 the
3 a
4 a
5 a
6 an

5
- •• Egypt, China
- •• Japan, Chinese
- ••• Portugal
- ••• Egyptian
- ••• Portuguese, Japanese

3C

1

Places	house, church, street, supermarket, factory, restaurant, office, school
People	woman, children, waiter, worker, driver
Transport	taxi, lorry, bus, bike

3
1 cities
2 countries
3 languages
4 cinemas
5 currencies
6 offices
7 men
8 women

4
1 drivers in their cars
2 people in shops
3 families in cinemas
4 workers in factories
5 children in churches

5
a 4
b 5
c 1
d 2
e 3

6
1 on
2 in
3 on
4 in
5 in
6 on
7 in
8 on

7
1 B
2 A
3 B
4 A
5 B
6 B
7 A
8 A
9 A

3D

1
1 Do
2 don't
3 Do
4 do
5 Do
6 don't
7 Do
8 do
9 Do
10 don't

2
1 I read Chinese quite well.
2 I write a little Chinese.
3 I understand Chinese very well.
4 I don't speak Chinese very well.
5 I pronounce Chinese quite well.
6 I know a little vocabulary.

3
1 We read German quite well.
2 We don't write German very well.
3 We understand German very well.
4 We speak a little German.
5 We don't pronounce German very well.

4
/s/ Spanish, France, South African, Swedish, Swahili, currency
/ʃ/ Spanish, Russian, Swedish, nationality, Egyptian, Polish

Skills Practice

1 bus stop, cash machines, toilets, South Street exit, chemist's

2
1 South Street exit
2 bus stop
3 chemist's
4 toilets
5 cash machines

3
1 Is there a bus stop near here?
2 Look, the cash machines are there.
3 I don't have my glasses with me.
4 At the other end of the shopping centre.
5 Oh yes, here it is!

5
1 False
2 False
3 True
4 False
5 True
6 True
7 False
8 True

6
1 c
2 a
3 b
4 e
5 d

7
a 2
b 1
c 3

10
1 flag
2 currency
3 language
4 nationality
5 what's
c Edinburgh

11 This is the Argentinian flag. The capital of Argentina is Buenos Aires and the language is Spanish. But what's the currency of Argentina?
b peso

Unit 4

4A

1 half-price, sold out, open, sorry we're full, please help yourself, no vacancies, private, cancelled, free entry, out of order, closed

3 1 no vacancies
2 half-price
3 cancelled
4 out of order
5 closed; open
6 private

4 1 c
2 a
3 d
4 b
5 e
6 g
7 j
8 i
9 h
10 f

5 a That's great!
b Oh really?
c Oh no!
d Oh no!
e That's great!
f Good luck!
g Good luck!
h That's great!
i I'm sorry!
j Oh really?

4B

1 1 Y
2 R
3 A
4 U
5 R
6 B
7 E
8 F
9 February

2 1 the seventh of April
2 the fifteenth of April
3 the fourth of August
4 the twentieth of August
5 the third of October
6 the ninth of October

4 1 on; at
2 on; at; in
3 in; on; at
4 at; on
5 on; at
6 at; in; on
7 in; on; at
8 at; on

5 1 What date is your birthday?
2 What time is your English class?
3 What day do you go shopping?
4 When are your summer holidays?

4C

1 **go** to work, back to bed, for a run, to the kitchen
get up, dressed
have breakfast, a shower, tea or coffee

2 1 c
2 b
3 f
4 a
5 d
6 e

3 1 is
2 starts
3 finishes
4 has
5 goes
6 reads
7 listens
8 plays
9 studies
10 watches

4 1 Where does he work?
2 When does he finish work?
3 What time does he get up?
4 What does he have for breakfast?
5 What does he do after breakfast?
6 Does he play football?
7 When does he get up late?

5 1 early
2 late
3 the mail
4 for a run
5 fruit for breakfast
6 the house
7 TV
8 her teeth
9 work

4D

1 1 to work
2 late for work
3 the newspaper
4 a coffee break
5 some letters
6 lunch
7 the boss
8 the clock
9 home

2 1 He always drives to work.
2 He doesn't often arrive early for work.
3 He often reads the newspaper.
4 He's never late for his coffee break.
5 He sometimes writes letters.
6 He often has lunch for two hours.
7 He doesn't usually listen to the boss.
8 He always looks at the clock.
9 He's always the first to leave work.

3 1 Do you like your job?
2 When do you go on holiday?
3 Where do you usually go?
4 Do you go with friends or family?
5 Do you use the car on holiday?

4 leave /iː/ mean, sleep, people, repeat, three
live /ɪ/ this, listen, finish, thing

Skills Practice

1 1 b
2 e
3 a
4 f
5 c
6 d

3 Austria, France, Germany, Holland, Italy

4 1 d
2 b
3 a
4 e
5 c
6 c

5 **A** So, Jack, you're a lorry driver. Tell me **about your** normal week.
J Normal week? **I don't have** any normal weeks! Yeah, well, I usually work **Monday to Friday**, but, erm, it's often **weekends** too.

7
Monday	**5.00** gym
Tuesday	**9.00–11.00** French class; **2.00** lunch; **3.00–9.00** work
Wednesday	**2.00** lunch
Thursday	**9.30–11.30** shopping; **3.00–9.00** work
Friday	**5.00** gym; **evening** out with friends
Saturday	**10.30** breakfast; **2.00** lunch; **evening** out with friends

8 1 True
2 False
3 True
4 True
5 True
6 False
7 False

9 usually; shopping; Tuesdays; people; Wednesday; bike; father; lessons; family

Unit 5

5A

1
1 Do you remember me?
2 Do you know my boyfriend?
3 Sorry, what's your name again?
4 I'm sorry, but I don't remember your name.
5 Come and meet them.

2
1 you; me
2 him; her
3 them; us
4 it

3
1 him
2 He
3 him
4 her
5 they
6 me
7 them
8 her
9 She
10 it

4
/əʊ/   o
/iː/   e
/eɪ/   a
/aɪ/   i
/juː/   u

5
a day, eight, say, play, name
e tea, three, speak, meet
i buy, five, nine, drive, like
o go, know, show
u you, rule, two, blue, school

5B

1
1 thin cat
2 white cat
3 new bike
4 small bike
5 short tree
6 new clock
7 short street
8 thin book
9 long hair

2
1 a big black taxi
2 two old grey buses
3 tall grey offices
4 a big new factory
5 four tall green trees
6 a new white bike
7 two fat white cats
8 a short blond man
9 a big black umbrella

3
1 h   6 j
2 e   7 k
3 c   8 i
4 a   9 f
5 b

4 /æ/ man   bag, have, cat, bank, fact, bad
/e/ men   get, spell, text, guess, very, friend, again

5C

1 Across
3 notebook
5 printer
6 battery
9 pencil
Down
1 rubber
2 computer
4 pen
7 ruler
8 file

2
1 've; haven't
2 Have; haven't
3 Have; have; 've
4 've; haven't

3
1 Have you got a car?
  No, I've got a motorbike.
2 Have you got any children?
  Yes, we've got two girls and a boy / a boy and two girls.
3 Have they got any pets?
  Yes, they've got two cats and a mouse / a mouse and two cats.

4
1 c
2 e
3 d
4 a
5 b

5D

1
1 d   5 b
2 a   6 e
3 f   7 h
4 c   8 g

2 *Example answers*
1 She's got an old computer, but he's got a new one.
2 She's got long hair, but he's got short hair.
3 She's got a big TV, but he's got a small one.
4 She's got a black cat, but he hasn't.
5 Her room's got five chairs, but his room's got four.
6 She's got a bottle of wine, but he's got water.
7 She's got a photo of a man, but he's got a photo of a woman.
8 She's got magazines on the table, but he's got books.
9 She's got a window, but he's got a poster on the wall.
10 She's got chocolates on the table, but he's got biscuits.

3
1 car
2 watch
3 dog
4 house
5 nice

Skills Practice

1

	No1	No3	No5
family	Smith	Patel	Kowalski
children	2	3	1 (boy)
transport	red car	2 cars	blue car
pets	grey cat	2 dogs	3 cats

	No2	No4	No6
family	Dixon	Molina	Jones
children	1 (girl)	2	no
transport	black car	grey car	motorbike
pets	no	rabbit	2 cats, 1 dog

2
a 3
b 2
c 3

3
a Henry meets Mr Patel
b Jenny meets Ricardo and Elena
c Stella meets Sheila

4
1 c
2 a
3 b
4 b/c
5 a
6 c

5
A Mr Patel! **How** are you?
B Fine, thanks, Mike. And you?
A **We're** fine, thank you. Do you know my brother Henry?
B No, I don't think so.
A Come and meet **him**.
  Henry, this is Mr Patel, **our** neighbour. Mr Patel, Henry, my **brother**.
C Nice to meet you!
B Yes, **you** too.

7
a 3
b 1
c 2

8
1 weekend
2 long
3 little
4 park
5 cat, dog
6 Indian, Chinese
7 techno, pop
8 tea, coffee
9 blue, brown, green, blond, white

9 He's short and bald but he's got lovely blue eyes. He works in an office and he loves Italian food. He drinks red wine every weekend. He doesn't watch much TV but he likes a good film. His name's Henry – he's my dad and he's OK.

Unit 6

6A

1 **Across**
3 biscuits
6 oranges
8 crisps
9 coffee
11 chocolates
12 apples

Down
1 milk
2 sandwiches
4 soup
5 tea
7 wine
10 water

2 **countable** chocolates, biscuits, oranges, crisps, apples, sandwiches
uncountable coffee, milk, soup, tea, wine, water

3 **countable** pens, newspapers, CDs, batteries, pencils
uncountable perfume, paper, ink

4
1	is	5	are
2	are	6	is
3	is	7	are
4	is		

5 1 **A** How much are the biscuits, please?
2 **B** They're €1 a packet.
3 **A** How much is the coffee?
4 **B** It's €1.30.
5 **A** OK. I'd like two cups of coffee and two packets of biscuits.
6 **B** That's €4.60, please.
7 **A** Here you are.
8 **B** Thank you.

6 How <u>much</u> are the <u>crisps</u>?
How <u>much</u> is the <u>wine</u>?
They're <u>one</u> euro <u>twenty</u>,
and <u>five</u> ninety-<u>nine</u>.

6B

1 1 fish and chips
2 bread and jam
3 sausage and eggs
4 toasted sandwich
5 chicken legs
6 apple pie
7 tomato salad
8 chocolate cake

2 **Meat** chicken legs, sausage and eggs
Fish fish and chips
Vegetables tomato salad
Others toasted sandwich, bread and jam, apple pie, chocolate cake

3 1 We've got some meat.
2 We haven't got any eggs.
3 We've got some fish.
4 We've got some tomatoes.
5 We haven't got any milk.
6 We haven't got any cake.
7 We've got some carrots.
8 We haven't got any sausages.

4
1	Can	5	have
2	like	6	don't
3	any	7	Would
4	some	8	please

5 /iː/ tree, week, speak, peas, cheese, three, tea, beans, please
other sounds break, bread, steak, great

6C

1 **Spaghetti Bolognese** pasta, meat, tomatoes, onions, cheese
Russian salad potatoes, egg, yogurt, fish, peas
Italian risotto chicken, rice, onions, carrots, salt

2 *Example answers*
1 In A there's some rice, but there isn't any pasta.
2 In B there aren't any oranges.
3 In A there's some sugar, but there isn't any salt.
4 In B there's some wine, but there isn't any milk.
5 In A there are some eggs, but there aren't any onions.
6 In B there isn't any fish.
7 In A there's some meat and in B there's some chicken.
8 In B there's some butter and some yogurt.

3 1 Are there any onions?
Yes, there are.
2 Are there any eggs?
No, there aren't.
3 Is there any yogurt?
Yes, there is.
4 Is there any rice?
No, there isn't.
5 Are there any apples?
No, there aren't.
6 Is there any sugar?
No, there isn't.

4 My <u>sister</u> likes an <u>actor</u>,
so she buys him a <u>flower</u>,
she sends him a <u>letter</u>,
but he <u>never</u> sends an <u>answer</u>.

6D

1 1 There isn't much butter.
2 There's a lot of milk.
3 There are a lot of eggs.
4 There isn't much bread.
5 There aren't many apples.
6 There isn't much coffee.
7 There are a lot of carrots.
8 There aren't many cakes.

2 1 How much butter is there?
2 How much milk is there?
3 How many eggs are there?
4 How much bread is there?
5 How many apples are there?
6 How much coffee is there?
7 How many carrots are there?
8 How many cakes are there?

3 1 Would you like a cup of coffee?
2 Do you take milk and sugar?
3 Would you like any toast?
4 Do you want butter or jam? / Do you want jam or butter?

4 some **bread** and **butter**
some **ham** and **eggs**
a **piece** of **pizza**
some **chicken legs**
some **tea** or **coffee**
with **milk** or **sugar**
What would you **like**?
a **glass** of **water**
– **please**!

Skills Practice

1
1	a	4	e
2	d	5	c
3	b		

2
1	4	5	5
2	3	6	1
3	4 and 5	7	4
4	6	8	1 and 2

3
1	2	5	4
2	6	6	1
3	3	7	5
4	5	8	3

5
a	4	c	3
b	1	d	2

6 1 **A** Is the food all right, madam?
2 **B** Yes, thank you. It's fine.
3 **A** Would you like any wine?
4 **B** Ah, yes, please.
5 **A** Red or white?
6 **B** Red, please.
7 **A** Would you like a bottle or glass?
8 **B** Oh, er, a bottle please. A bottle of red wine.
9 **A** Thank you, madam.

8
1	food	4	any
2	usually	5	much
3	some		

9 My **favourite** food is Italian. It's called risotto and my **aunt** makes a delicious one. It's got rice and **beans** and **meat**, and lots of vegetables – **onions**, **carrots**, **peas** and tomatoes. Oh, and some **cheese** too. And we usually have a **bottle** of red wine with it.

Unit 7

7A

1
1 fishing
2 sailing
3 guitar
4 basketball
5 cards
6 roller-skating
7 a run
8 the gym
9 a swim
10 the park
11 a walk
12 table tennis

2

go	fishing, sailing, roller-skating
go for	a run, a swim, a walk
go to	the gym, the park
play	basketball, cards, table tennis
play the	guitar

4

a	1	d	4
b	5	e	6
c	3	f	2

5
1 often
2 What
3 go
4 there
5 swim
6 ever
7 not
8 buy

7B

1
1 It's rainy and cool.
2 It's sunny and hot.
3 It's cloudy and warm.
4 It's snowy and cold.
5 It's rainy and cool.
6 It's rainy and hot.
7 It's cloudy and cold.
8 It's windy and warm.
9 It's cloudy and warm.
10 It's snowy and cold.

2
1 have
2 watching
3 go
4 some music
5 fishing
6 going
7 go
8 a DVD
9 play
10 reading

3 *Example answers*
1 How about going to the shops?
2 How about watching a film? / Let's watch a film.
3 How about playing cards? / Let's play cards.
4 How about playing table tennis? / Let's play table tennis.
5 How about going cycling? / Let's go cycling.
6 How about going for a swim? / Let's go for a swim.
7 How about playing football? / Let's play football.
8 How about going for a run? / Let's go for a run.

4
1 **A** It's ten o'clock. What shall we do today?
2 **B** I don't know. What would you like to do?
3 **A** How about a game of tennis?
4 **B** Oh, it's cloudy and cold!
5 **A** Well, roller-skating is warm! Let's go roller-skating.
6 **B** I haven't got any roller-skates.
7 **A** OK - **you** make a suggestion!
8 **B** Let's just stay in!

5 weather, what, answer, question, windy, when, snow, week, swim, view, where, how, why, write

7C

1
1 g
2 e
3 d
4 b
5 h
6 a
7 c
8 f

2
1 can't
2 can't
3 can
4 can't
5 Can
6 can

3
1 slowly
2 easily
3 well
4 badly
5 quickly

4 *Example answers*
1 Bob can drive, but not very well.
2 Lucy can drive very well.
3 Lucy can use a computer very well.
4 Bob can read Chinese, but not very well.
5 Lucy can't read Chinese.
6 Bob can't speak Chinese but Lucy can.

5
1 bus
2 fast
3 Spanish
4 anything
5 football
6 name

7D

1
1 meeting
2 doing
3 playing
4 listening to
5 going
6 talking
7 watching
8 taking
9 reading

3
1 I like dogs but I don't like taking them for a walk!
2 I like films on TV and I love watching them at the cinema.
3 I love going to the beach but I don't like the mountains.
4 I like reading books but I don't enjoy magazines.
5 I love talking to friends but I don't like using the Internet.
6 I enjoy a good meal but I don't like cooking!
7 I like watching sports but I don't like playing them!
8 I love drinking tea but I don't like making it.
9 I enjoy eating but I hate dog biscuits!

4
1 Do you like cooking?
2 What meals can you cook?
3 What do you like doing at weekends?
4 Do you do any exercise?
5 What do you enjoy doing in the holidays?
6 What things do you dislike?

5
1 Hello Henry!
2 house and home
3 half an hour
4 Who works hard?
5 She hates the housework!
6 When's your holiday?
7 I need help with my homework!

Skills Practice

1
1 hotel
2 restaurants
3 shops
4 bars
5 hairdresser's
6 gym
7 river
8 park
9 swimming pool
10 disco
11 car park
12 cinema

2
1 Have you got that?
2 All right?
3 OK?
4 Can you see that?
5 Any questions?

4
1 Young Children
2 Teenagers
3 Adults
4 Pets

5
1 True
2 False
3 True
4 False
5 True
6 True
7 False
8 True
9 False
10 False

7
1 ✓ talking about herself
2 ✓ her work
3 ✓ breakfast in bed
4 ✓ visiting friends
5 ✗ cooking
6 ✓ getting up late
7 ✗ washing dishes
8 ✓ her dogs

8
1 c
2 f
3 d
4 e
5 a
6 b

9
1 two months
2 half an hour
3 work on Sundays
4 or play sports
5 On their last day off

Unit 8

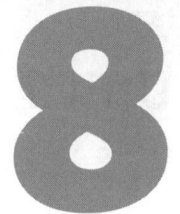

8A

1
1. for a walk
2. for a coffee
3. to the shops
4. for a run
5. to the gym
6. to the cinema
7. for a drink
8. to the pool
9. to the park

2
1. **A** Hi, Jerry. Are you busy?
2. **B** No, not really. Why?
3. **A** I'm going to the shops. Would you like to come?
4. **B** The shops?
5. **A** Yeah, I need some things.
6. **B** What time is it?
7. **A** It's 11.30.
8. **B** Oh dear! Sorry, but I haven't got time. I need to start cooking lunch!
9. **A** OK, no problem.

3
1. to dance
2. a drink
3. go to Paris
4. a coffee
5. to go out
6. an apple
7. to be
8. a walk
9. to go

4
1. four; to
2. to; to; to
3. for; two
4. for; to; to; two

8B

1
1. Michael
2. Michael
3. Theresa
4. Michael
5. Bernard
6. Helen

2
1. jeans and a T-shirt
2. a shirt and tie
3. a hat and coat
4. a jacket and trousers
5. shorts and sandals
6. boots and shoes
7. a suit and a dress
8. a short skirt and a long skirt
9. a sweater and a cap

3
1	c	6	g
2	d	7	h
3	j	8	e
4	a	9	f
5	b	10	i

4
1. shirts
2. work
3. board
4. third
5. shorts
6. working
7. bird
8. fourth

8C

1
1. sitting
2. drinking
3. laughing
4. looking at
5. playing
6. dancing
7. smiling
8. using
9. writing

2
1. He's sitting on a desk.
2. She's dancing to the music.
3. He's laughing.
4. Is she writing in a notebook?
5. Is he using the phone?
6. She's playing computer games.
7. He's smiling.
8. They're looking at photos.
9. He's drinking coffee.

3
1. are you doing
2. I'm listening to
3. are they doing
4. is talking
5. is she saying
6. She's talking
7. they're talking

4
1. nothing
2. speaking
3. car
4. park
5. bike
6. dinner
7. exercises
8. bath
9. you

8D

1
1. gets up; she's having
2. isn't going
3. takes; she's taking
4. arrives; she's going
5. is waiting; has
6. looks; is looking at
7. goes; is flying
8. is having

2
1. meets
2. travels
3. eats
4. is / 's wearing
5. is / 's carrying
6. is / 's drinking
7. is writing
8. is watching
9. is / 's wearing
10. are you doing

3
1. they; us
2. she; him
3. he; her
4. she; him
5. they; us
6. he; her

Skills Practice

1
1. M
2. MW
3. MW
4. W
5. MW
6. MW
7. W
8. MW
9. M
10. MW

2
1. False
2. True
3. False
4. True
5. False
6. False
7. False

4 a

5
1. a tall man
2. short grey hair
3. a long black coat
4. a black tie
5. white shoes

7
a	2
b	3
c	1

8
1. c
2. a
3. e
4. b
5. d

9
1. is
2. love
3. has
4. puts
5. got
6. boring

10 dangerous; important; terrified; silly; good

Unit 9

9A

1
1. c
2. e
3. f
4. d
5. b
6. a

2
1. departure gate
2. plane
3. airport
4. taxi
5. underground station
6. train
7. bus station
8. bus
9. train station

3
1. R
2. P
3. P
4. R
5. P
6. R
7. R
8. P

9B

1
Across
3. police station
5. lights
7. church
9. bank
10. bookshop
11. bridge
Down
1. restaurant
2. castle
4. post office
6. phone box
8. car park
9. bus stop

2
1. to; left; straight; first; on
2. right; on; left
3. out; turn; on; opposite

3
1. It's the first left at the corner.
2. There's a bank at the corner.
3. The post office is just opposite.
4. Go straight on and turn left at the lights.
5. The map says there's an art gallery near here.
6. It's across the bridge and on the left.
7. Turn right again into Union Street.
8. I think there's a tourist information office in the station.

9C

1
1. noisy
2. crowded
3. polite
4. wet
5. friendly
6. uncomfortable
7. delicious
8. empty

2
positive clean, lovely, beautiful, comfortable, polite, exciting, delicious, interesting, fantastic

negative dirty, horrible, boring, unfriendly, uncomfortable, awful

3
1. Were
2. was
3. Were
4. wasn't
5. Was
6. was
7. Were
8. weren't
9. Were
10. were
11. was
12. was
13. Were
14. weren't
15. Were
16. were

4 is; are; is; are; are

5 was; was; were; was; was

9D

1
1. happened
2. looked
3. noticed
4. relaxed
5. walked
6. decided
7. stayed
8. played
9. talked
10. wanted

2
1. happened
2. wanted
3. decided
4. stayed
5. relaxed
6. played
7. talked
8. walked
9. looked
10. noticed

3
1. I walked up the hill
2. to the Nightmare Hotel
3. I stopped at the door
4. but I couldn't see the bell
5. I knocked and I waited
6. in the cold and windy night
7. I looked in the window
8. but there wasn't any light

4 He waited at the bus stop.
It started to rain.
He opened his umbrella.
A voice asked him to help.
He answered her question.
They walked into town.
They talked all the way.
And who knows what happened after that!

Skills Practice

1
a. 3
b. 5
c. 4
d. 1
e. 2

2 Cork, Baltimore, Skull, Bear Island, Valentia Island, Castleisland, Newcastle West, Limerick

3
1. d
2. a
3. h
4. g
5. c
6. b
7. f
8. e

4
a. 2
b. 3
c. 5
d. 4
e. 1

5
1. False
2. True
3. False
4. False
5. True
6. False

6 Well, I went to France **last summer**, on a **cheap holiday**. I stayed in youth hostels, you know, where **you can meet** lots of **young people**, and, er, they tell you all the **good places** to visit.

8
a. 3
b. 1
c. 5
d. 2
e. 4

9
1. e
2. a
3. f
4. b
5. d
6. c

10 & 11
uncle	*noun*
cousins	*noun*
country	*noun*
friendly	*adjective*
delicious	*adjective*
beach	*noun*
aunt	*noun*
expensive	*adjective*

Unit 10

10A

1
1	f	5	a
2	h	6	d
3	g	7	b
4	c	8	e

2
1 Where did the schoolchildren go?
2 What did they visit?
3 Who did they meet?
4 What did they ask her?
5 What did the children say?
6 What did Julia buy?
7 When did they arrive home?

3
a	1	e	2
b	6	f	4
c	5	g	7
d	3		

4
1	b	5	f
2	c	6	a
3	h	7	d
4	e	8	g

10B

1
1 left
2 bought
3 drove
4 got
5 had
6 joined
7 became
8 met
9 saw
10 sold
11 started
12 worked

2
1 left
2 got
3 had
4 worked
5 met
6 saw
7 joined
8 drove
9 bought
10 started
11 became
12 sold

3
1 wrote
2 rides
3 sent
4 Batman
5 hard
6 down

5
1a left school
1b got a job as a lorry driver
1c drove a lorry for five years
1d bought his own lorry

2a went to university
2b became a teacher
2c went abroad
2d got married

10C

1
1 rode; didn't ride
2 got; didn't get
3 paid; didn't pay
4 drank; didn't drink
5 wrote; didn't write
6 put; didn't put
7 left; didn't leave

2
1 What was it about?
2 Why was she angry?
3 What did she do?
4 What did he tell her?
5 What did the wife do?
6 Did she use poison?
7 Did her husband die in the bath?
8 What did she do with the body?
9 What did she say to the police?
10 What happened in the end?

3
1 Where did you go yesterday?
2 When did you finish work?
3 Did you go straight home?
4 Which shops did you visit?
5 Who did you meet?
6 Did you kill your husband?

10D

1 **Across**
4 physics
6 medicine
7 secondary
9 degree
13 literature
14 primary
Down
1 music
2 languages
3 high school
5 university
8 chemistry
10 diploma
11 history
12 art

2
1 literature; diploma
2 chemistry; university; degree
3 history; high school

3
1969 nineteen sixty-nine
2006 two thousand and six
1908 nineteen oh eight
1836 eighteen thirty-six
1998 nineteen ninety-eight
1950 nineteen fifty
2025 two thousand and twenty-five

4
1 Greenpeace
2 blue eyes
3 Police!
4 Yes, Miss
5 plays in the theatre
6 these books

Skills Practice

1
1 When he was a boy
2 When he was 17
3 at age 18
4 For the next 20 years
5 When he died in 1944

3
1 False
2 True
3 False
4 True
5 False

4
1 c
2 b
3 c

5
a	3
b	2
c	1
d	6
e	5
f	4

6 The **cat** was sick, so the woman took it to the **vet's** clinic, but it died. She tried to kill the vet, first with poisoned **chocolates**, second with a poisoned **book**, and third with a **gun**.

8
1 c
2 a
3 b

9
1 experience
2 company
3 fluent
4 expenses
5 health insurance
6 excellent
7 team
8 skills
9 manager

11
1 and
2 and
3 and
4 and
5 but
6 and

12
1 c
2 a
3 d
4 e
5 b

Unit 11

11A

1
bed and breakfast
hotel
campsite
self-catering apartment
youth hostel
tent

2
1 bed and breakfast
2 tent
3 youth hostel
4 campsite
5 self-catering apartment
6 hotel

3
1 isn't warm enough
2 is too expensive
3 isn't big enough
4 is too hot
5 is too dirty
6 is too slow
7 isn't interesting enough
8 isn't quiet enough
9 are too far

4
1	3	5	3
2	4	6	3
3	3	7	3
4	4	8	5

5
● ● ●   adjective, exercise, interview, sentences, syllables
● ● ● ●   conversation, information
● ● ● ● ●   vocabulary

11B

1
1 toilet
2 bath
3 cupboard
4 shower
5 washbasin
6 sofa
7 table
8 chairs
9 sink
10 fridge
11 cooker

2
1 There aren't enough tables.
2 There are too many chairs.
3 There isn't enough juice.
4 There's too much wine.
5 There isn't enough food.
6 There aren't enough glasses.
7 There aren't enough CDs.
8 There isn't enough space for dancing.

3
short vowel sound: 1 vowel symbol
gym, golf, shop, sink, hot, pub
long vowel sound: 2 vowel symbols
stay, town, drive
long vowel sound: 1 vowel + :
view, beach, park, tea, walk, farm

11C

1
1	soft	6	dirty
2	cold	7	new
3	long	8	thin
4	modern	9	expensive
5	small	10	comfortable

2
1 fatter
2 cooler
3 more comfortable
4 warmer
5 better
6 dirtier
7 smaller
8 longer

3
1 Ricky's car is faster than Frank's.
2 Frank's car is dirtier than Ricky's.
3 Ricky's car is more comfortable than Frank's.
4 Frank's car is older than Ricky's.
5 Ricky's car is better than Frank's.
6 Ricky's car is more expensive than Frank's.
7 Frank's car is worse than Ricky's.

4
Winter sleep
The days become shorter not longer
The weather becomes colder not warmer
Inside is warmer than outside
His eyes become smaller then close
Sleep the winter sleep
Wait for a better life in the spring

11D

1
1 bedroom   bed, chair, shelf
2 living room   sofa, coffee table, chair
3 kitchen   table, shelf, dining table, chair
4 office   desk, shelf, chair

3
1	fast	6	strongest
2	happiest	7	softest
3	lowest	8	most useful
4	fastest	9	strongest
5	most useful		

4
1 the cheapest
2 the longest
3 the shortest
4 the most modern
5 the most old-fashioned
6 the hottest
7 the coolest
8 the highest
9 the lowest
10 the most expensive

5
1 A is the cheapest. C is the most expensive.
2 A is the highest. B is the lowest.
3 A is the shortest. C is the longest.
4 A is the hottest. C is the coldest.
5 A is the most modern. B is the most old-fashioned.

6
1 a bottle of wine
2 a plate of beans
3 a piece of paper
4 a wonderful view
5 a white bathroom washbasin
6 we have pink, white, or black shelves

Skills Practice

1
1 Transport
2 Accommodation
3 Clothes
4 Food
5 People

2
1 reasonable prices
2 budget
3 cotton
4 protect
5 lamb
6 in advance

3
1	False	5	True
2	True	6	False
3	False	7	False
4	False	8	False

5
1	b	4	c
2	c	5	b
3	a		

6
a	1	e	4
b	6	f	2
c	3	g	5
d	7		

7
fridge   kitchen
heating   towels
toilet paper

8
1	c	3	a
2	b		

9
1	c	4	e
2	d	5	a
3	b		

10
1 My family and I are in apartment number six, and **we have a problem**.
2 Just a moment please. Could you **repeat that more** slowly?
3 Now, could you just give **me your name**?
4 And what time **did you arrive** at the apartment?
5 And what's the **number of your** apartment?

12
1 a quiet part of town
2 from the shops
3 a lot of noise
4 from the living room
5 the biggest room
6 opposite the TV
7 at the other end
8 one of the walls

13

Unit 12

12A

1 **Across**
4 bank manager
6 vet
7 teacher
9 optician
10 shopkeeper

Down
1 dentist
2 farmer
3 mechanic
5 hairdresser
8 doctor

2 1 shopkeeper
2 optician
3 bank manager
4 dentist
5 vet
6 hairdresser
7 mechanic
8 teacher

3 1 Mid-afternoon tomorrow.
2 First thing tomorrow morning.
3 Mid-morning tomorrow.
4 Late tomorrow morning.
5 The day after tomorrow.
6 Early tomorrow evening.
7 Tomorrow night.

4 1 C 6 A
2 A 7 C
3 A 8 A
4 C 9 A
5 C 10 C

12B

1 1 hands; head
2 hand; stomach; hand; back
3 head; legs; hands; feet
4 foot; heart; arm; neck
5 hands; back
6 feet; neck; hands; stomach

2 1 c, e, g 3 a, h
2 d 4 b, f

3 1 b, d, g
2 e, f
3 a, c

4 1 wrong 5 with
2 ache 6 fine
3 much 7 housework
4 don't 8 headache

5 **short vowel sound** /æ/
hat, cat, hand, back
long vowel sound /ɑː/
heart, arm, car, start, half, park
short vowel sound /e/
leg, friend, head, twelve, weather
long vowel sound /eɪ/
stay, pain, they, game, eight

12C

1 1 doing 6 playing
2 preparing 7 putting
3 going 8 coming
4 having 9 taking
5 cooking 10 helping

2 1 are you doing
2 'm helping
3 'm cooking
4 'm going
5 're taking
6 'm playing
7 is coming
8 're having
9 're putting
10 're preparing

3 1 are going shopping
2 are driving
3 are having lunch
4 are visiting
5 are buying gifts / are going shopping
6 are having dinner
7 are watching

12D

1 1 What are you going to be when you grow up?
I'm not going to be a doctor. I'm going to be a footballer.
2 Where are you going on holiday?
We're going to visit the north of Germany. We're not / We aren't going to stay in the south.
3 What are you going to do with the car?
He's going to drive, so he's not / he isn't going to drink.
4 What are you going to study at university?
I'm going to think about it for a while. I'm not going to decide until next year.

2 1 I 5 A
2 A 6 I
3 A 7 A
4 A 8 I

3 1 She's going to phone Helen.
2 She's meeting John at the airport on Friday.
3 She's going shopping with Mum on Thursday morning.
4 She's taking the children to the dentist for their appointments.
5 She's having a parents' meeting at school on Friday at 4.30.
6 She's going to work in the garden.
7 She's going to Paula's wedding.
8 She's going to sit down and relax.

4 1 d 5 c
2 e 6 b
3 f 7 h
4 a 8 g

5 1 N 5 F
2 F 6 N
3 F 7 N
4 N 8 F

Skills Practice

1 1 bank Thursday 11 a.m.
2 dentist today 4.15 p.m.
3 mechanic's Monday 12 p.m.
4 hairdresser's Friday 6 p.m.

2 a 2 e 1
b 4 f 1
c 1 g 2
d 3 h 3

3 1 I'd like to make an appointment to speak to the manager, please.
2 One moment, please. OK, which day were you thinking of?
3 Some time this week, before the weekend.
4 Right, thank you Mr Brunel. That's next Thursday at eleven in the morning.

5 Monday **9–12** classes; **1.30** shopping centre; **night** studying for exam
Tuesday **morning** exam; **12.00** dentist; **3.30** meet in the park; **4.00** football match; **night** Satomi's party
Wednesday **morning** cleaning; **1.00** lunch; **8.30** cinema

6 a supermarket
b hairdresser's
c optician's
d garage

7 1 b
2 a and b
3 5.30
4 a
5 free oil change
6 a
7 £10 or more
8 d

9 1 invitation
2 happy
3 love
4 company
5 say
6 show
7 wonderful

OXFORD
UNIVERSITY PRESS

Great Clarendon Street, Oxford OX2 6DP

Oxford University Press is a department of the University of Oxford.
It furthers the University's objective of excellence in research, scholarship,
and education by publishing worldwide in

Oxford New York

Auckland Cape Town Dar es Salaam Hong Kong Karachi
Kuala Lumpur Madrid Melbourne Mexico City Nairobi
New Delhi Shanghai Taipei Toronto

With offices in

Argentina Austria Brazil Chile Czech Republic France Greece
Guatemala Hungary Italy Japan Poland Portugal Singapore
South Korea Switzerland Thailand Turkey Ukraine Vietnam

OXFORD and OXFORD ENGLISH are registered trade marks of
Oxford University Press in the UK and in certain other countries

© Oxford University Press 2008

The moral rights of the author have been asserted

Database right Oxford University Press (maker)

First published 2008
2012
10 9 8 7

ISBN: 978 0 19 430490 0

Printed in China

English **Result**

Elementary

Workbook Answer Key Booklet

McKenna

OXFORD
UNIVERSITY PRESS

www.oup.com/elt

for all your
testing needs
online go to

oxfordenglishtesting.com

CEF
B1
A2
A1

OXFORD ENGLISH
ISBN 978-0-19-430490-0

9 780194 304900

OXFORD

English Result

Joe McKenna

How to **say hello**

A **Vocabulary** greeting phrases

1 Match the pictures and phrases.

 a ☐   b ☐   c ☐

1 Good afternoon! 2 Good evening! 3 Good morning!

2 Complete the conversations.

What's your name again   Oops   What's your name
~~Hello~~   And you   My name's

Day 1

A ¹ *Hello*_____!

B Hello! ²_____?

A My name's Bob.

B Sorry? ³_____?

A Bob. My name's Bob. Nice to meet you!

Day 2

B Hello again, Jim.

A Hello, Jennifer. ⁴_____ Bob.

B ⁵_____! Hello, Bob. How are you?

A I'm fine, thanks. ⁶_____?

B I'm fine.

3 Put the conversation in order.

☐ Oops! Hello, Jennifer. How are you?
☐ Hello, Bob! My name's Jennifer!
☐ I'm fine too.
☐ I'm fine thanks. And you?
1 Hello again, Julia!

B **Pronunciation** rhythm and stress

4 **1A.1▶** Listen and tick ✓ the names you hear.

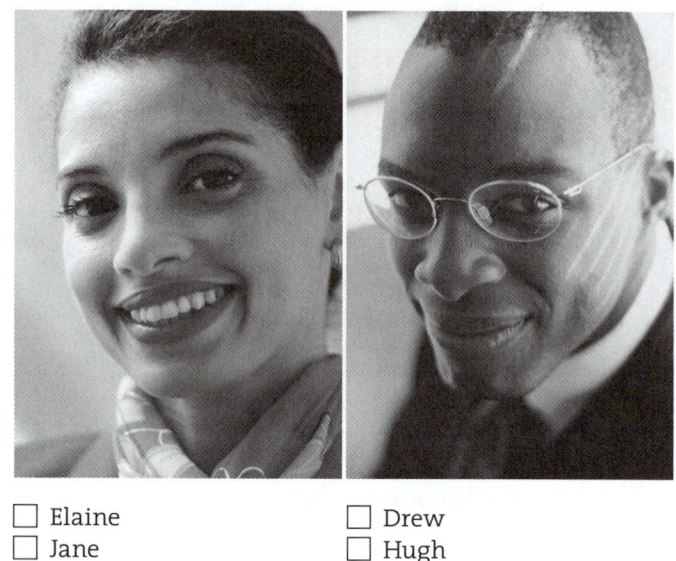

☐ Elaine   ☐ Drew
☐ Jane   ☐ Hugh
☐ Germaine   ☐ Stu

5 Listen again. Write the names.

A Hello, good	**mor**ning!	**What's** your	**name?**	
B Hello, good	**mor**ning!	**My** name's	¹_____.	
A **Nice** to	**meet** you!	**My** name's	²_____.	
B Hello,	³_____.	**Nice** to meet	**you!**	

6 Listen again and practise saying the sentences.

And you? Complete the conversation.

A Hi! What's your name?

You _____. And you?

A I'm Alan. How are you?

You _____

A OK! See you later!

You _____

How well can you say hello and ask people's names now?
Go back to the Student's Book >> p.7 and tick ✓ the line again.

G possessives *my, your, his, her*   V letters and numbers   P letters and numbers

A **Pronunciation** letters and numbers

1 **1B.1▶** Listen and correct the mistakes.

1 Phone numbers

Small, JC, 27 Butlin Rd......................................	~~3~~8946652
Smith, PA, 3 Stratford Pl.....................................	0997411
Smith, RS, 91 Brisbane Ave...............................	4065589
Spigott, LP, 144 Mitchell Dr.............................	2213074

2 Email addresses

@ **Patty** iou20@buzby.net	**Carla** quick14@spt.com
Tomas okchen@fanzine.	**Linda** lin3@livebird.org

3 Websites

SHOP ONLINE		
For music	▶	**www.toptunes.esl**
For medicine	▶	**www.qgetwell.co.uk**
For photos	▶	**www.digipiks.net**
For books	▶	**www.riadit.net**

B **Vocabulary** letters and numbers

A = 1	H = 8	O = 15	V = 22
B = 2	I = 9	P = 16	W = 23
C = 3	J = 10	Q = 17	X = 24
D = 4	K = 11	R = 18	Y = 25
E = 5	L = 12	S = 19	Z = 26
F = 6	M = 13	T = 20	
G = 7	N = 14	U = 21	

Example   13 - 25   14 - 1 - 13 - 5   9 - 19   18 - 5 - 24
          My   name   is   Rex.

2 What is the message?

7 - 15 - 15 - 4   13 - 15 - 18 - 14 - 9 - 14 - 7 !

_____ _____ !

8 - 15 - 23   1 - 18 - 5   25 - 15 - 21 ?

_____ _____ _____ ?

3 Write your own message in numbers.

_____

C **Grammar** possessives *my, your, his, her*

4 Complete the conversations with these words.

   my *her* *his* *your*

1 **A** Hello! What's
      your ____ name?
   B I'm Craig. And you?
   A _____ name's
      Gemma.
   B Nice to meet you!

2 **B** Mm! What's
      _____ name?
   A Irvina.
   B And what's
      _____
      phone number?
   A It's 77 33 74.

3 **A** Mm! What's
      _____ name?
   B Serge.
   A And what's
      _____
      phone number?
   B I don't know.

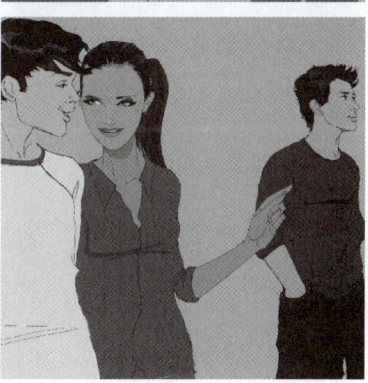

And you? Answer the questions.
What's your name?
What's your phone number?
And what's your email address?

g pronouns and possessives; present simple of *be* ⊞   v parts of an address; numbers 20+   P stress in questions

A Vocabulary numbers 20+

1 Write the answers in numbers.

1 thirteen + nine = _22_
2 forty – three = ____
3 twenty-seven + seventeen = ____
4 eighty-five – fifteen = ____
5 a hundred and six + twelve = ____
6 a hundred and thirty – sixty-five = ____
7 eleven + forty-two = ____
8 ninety-nine – ten = ____
9 a hundred – four = ____
10 sixty-seven + thirty-four = ____

2 Complete the crossword.

Across **2** 82 **5** 76 **7** 31 **8** 50 **9** 40
Down **1** 49 **3** 22 **4** 33 **6** 94

(crossword grid with 2 across starting: e i g h t y - t w o)

B Grammar pronouns and possessives; present simple of *be* ⊞

3 Match the pronouns with *am*, *is*, or *are*.

1 I _am = I'm_
2 he _____
3 she _____
4 we _____
5 they _____

4 Complete the sentences with your answers from exercise 3 and these words.

his   her   my   our   their

1 _I'm_ from Germany.
   _____ name's Helga.

2 _____ from Poland. _____ name's Iwona.
3 _____ from Russia. _____ name's Sergei.

4 _____ from China. _____ names are Lee and Ting.
5 _____ from Canada. _____ names are Marc and Claire.

C Pronunciation stress in questions

5 Match the questions and answers.

1 [c] **What's** your **first** name?   a P-A-L-M-E-R.
2 ☐ **What's** your **sur**name?   b 42 Ashford Street, Toronto.
3 ☐ **How** do you **spell** that?   c ~~Claire.~~
4 ☐ **Where** are you **from**?   d Palmer.
5 ☐ **What's** your ad**dress**?   e Canada.

6 **1C.1**▶ Listen and check.

7 Listen again and copy the stress.

And you? Answer the questions from exercise 5.

1
2
3
4
5

How well can you give your name and address now?
Go back to the Student's Book >> p.11 and tick ✓ the line again.

How to **start a conversation**

G present simple of *be* ⊞□? **V** *Mr, Mrs, Ms, Miss*; polite words and phrases

A Vocabulary polite words and phrases

1 Complete the conversations with these words.

please   thanks   sorry   thank you   excuse me

1 **A** _Excuse_ _me_____, two coffees, _____.
  B Here you are.
  A _____ _____ very much!

2 **A** How are you, James?
  B I'm fine, _____. And you?

3 **A** Hello, Miss Jones.
  B It's Ms Jones!
  A Oh, _____!

4 **A** _____ I'm late!
  B That's OK, sit down.
  A _____!

5 **A** _____ _____, what's your name again?
  B Sally.
  A Hi, Sally. I'm Jake.

B Grammar present simple of *be* ⊞□?

2 Underline the correct words.

1 'We're / You're Coldplay. We're / You're from England.'
2 Julia Roberts is / are American. He's / She's single.
3 'Hi, my name's Jean Reno. I'm / He's not American
  – I'm / He's French!'
4 Ewan McGregor is from Scotland. He's / It's a country
  in Europe. Is / Are he single? No – I'm / He's single.
5 Mel Gibson and Robyn Gibson is / are single. Sorry,
  that's not right. We're / They're married.
6 Celine Dion am / is Canadian. She isn't / aren't single,
  she's / he's married.

3 Match 1–6 with a–f.

1 [d] Are you   a you from?
2 [ ] Is your   b a teacher?
3 [ ] What's   c name Ewan?
4 [ ] Where are   d ~~married?~~
5 [ ] Is your mum e old are you?
6 [ ] How   f your phone number?

4 Match the answers with the questions in exercise 3.

a [1] No, I'm single.
b [ ] I'm 26.
c [ ] 07700 900443.
d [ ] No, my name's Ian.
e [ ] Yes, she is.
f [ ] I'm from London.

And you? Complete the conversation.

You Excuse me, _____ _____ from Germany?
B Yes, I am. And you?
You I'm from _____. What's your name?
B My name's Ulrich.
You I'm _____. _____!
B Nice to meet you! Are you married?
You _____. And you?
B No, I'm not. I'm single.
You Oh. Coffee?
B Yes, please!

How well can you start a conversation now?
Go back to the Student's Book ›› p.13 and tick ✓ the line again.

7

A Read for detail

1 Read the business cards and complete the table.

UNIVERSITY OF LENINGRAD

Ivana Kuznetsov

Department of Organic Chemistry

Ulitsa Rynok 27, Novgorod, Russia

TEL: 667 4321   EMAIL: kuznetsov@len.ac.ru

PQ OIL
CORPORATION

Brian J. Wilson
Accounts Manager

• 37 Queen St, Toronto, Canada
• Tel: 0909 8790981
• Email: bjwilson@pqoil.net

Enrique Delgado | Sales Representative

c. Manzanares 16-4-A ▪ 28017 Madrid ▪ Spain

℻ 0191 498 0996
🖰 edelgado17@spc.net

Yvonne Chanut

INTERPRETER & TRANSLATOR

Rue Bruxelles 16
69002 Lyon   *Tel:* 01632 960 0120
France   *Email:* yvchan@servling.net

Name	Country	Phone Number	Email address
			kuznetsov@len.ac.ru
	Canada		
		01632 960 0120	
Enrique Delgado			

2 Now write your own business card. Use your dictionary to check your job in English.

B Listen for key words and phrases

3 **15.1▶** Listen and complete these forms.

1

First name Marwan
Surname _____
Age _____
Marital status single
Country _____
Home address Marienstraat 37, Utrecht
Telephone 623 579210
Email _____
ID no. NED39462H

2

FIRST NAME	HOME ADDRESS
_____	67 Durban St, Pretoria
SURNAME	**TELEPHONE**
van der Post	_____
AGE	**EMAIL**
29	gilvdp@saturnus.net
MARITAL STATUS	**ID NO.**
_____	_____
COUNTRY	
S. Africa	

3

First name _____
Surname Collins
Age _____
Marital status _____
Country Ireland
Home address 4 Cathedral St, Cork
Telephone 202 7300
Email scorker@gtv.net
ID no. _____

4 Listen again. Match the phrases with the conversations.
1 ☐ Sorry?
2 ☐ Can you just repeat that?
3 ☐ How do you spell your surname? *(1)*
4 ☐ Could you spell that for me?
5 ☐ Two more questions.
6 ☐ Four more questions, please.

5 Check the audio script on >> p.91.

C Read and check information

6 Tick ✓ the true sentences and correct the false sentences.

1 Marwan is 45. *He's 35.*
2 He's from Utrecht, in Holland. ✓
3 His phone number is 632 579210.

4 Gillian is married.
5 Her home is in Pretoria.
6 She has no email address.

7 Sean's first name is Collins.
8 His passport number is 202 7300.
9 He's not married.
10 He's 31.

D Write personal information

7 Fill in the form with your personal details.

First name	_____
Surname	_____
Age	_____
Marital status	_____
Country	_____
Home address	_____
Telephone	_____
Email	_____
ID no.	_____

8 What does it say on forms in your language? Are any words the same or similar?

	in your language
First name	
Surname	
Age	
Marital status	
Country	
Home address	
Telephone	
Email	
ID no.	

E Read for detail

9 Read the letter and correct sentences 1–8.

Crown Hotel
15 Carlisle Road
Dumfries
24.7.07

Dear Helen,

Hello! How are you?

This is a photograph of me in Scotland. The other people in the picture are Yves, Sandra and Johann. They're my friends. Yves is a student here, and he's from Belgium. Sandra and Johann are also students. They're married, and they're from Germany. We are in a café having lunch. I meet new people every day – it's great!

There's no telephone in my room, but my mobile number is 07700 900 787, if you want to call. There are computers with the Internet in the hotel. My email address is gilvdp@saturnus.net.

Say hello to Tom and Tina for me!

Love,
Gillian

1 The letter is from ~~Helen~~. *Gillian*
2 Gillian is in England.
3 Yves and Sandra are married.
4 Johann is from Belgium.
5 Gillian is in class.
6 There is a telephone in her room.
7 Sandra's mobile number is 07700 900 887.
8 There are computers in the café.

F Write an address

10 Put this address in order.
☐ Ireland
☐ 4 Cathedral St.
1 Mr S. Collins
☐ Cork

11 Write a friend's name and address.

....
....
....
....

Now try the Self check on >> p.76.

How to **use English in the classroom**

G imperatives **V** English in the classroom **P** counting syllables

A Vocabulary English in the classroom

1 Complete the words with *a, e, i, o,* or *u.*

1 p e nc i l   2 p_ct_r_   3 _mbr_ll_

4 w_nd_w   5 st_d_nt   6 m_p

7 d_sk   8 ch__r   9 t__ch_r   10 b__rd

2 Read the conversations. Put the questions in order.

A Excuse me! English in what's this
¹ *What's this in English* _____?
B It's a picture.
A Sorry? please that you repeat can
² _____?
B A picture.
A spell you do how that
³ _____?
B P-I-C-T-U-R-E.
A Thank you!

A Open the window, please!
B slowly that can say please you
⁴ _____?
A Open the window.
B Thank you. that write please you can
⁵ _____?
A Yes. Look at the board.

B Grammar imperatives

3 Complete the instructions with the best word.
~~read~~ ~~write~~ ~~listen~~ ~~open~~ ~~close~~ ~~look~~ ~~ask~~

read write listen ~~open~~ close look ask

1 *open*_____ the umbrella
2 _____ a question
3 _____ on the board
4 _____ the window
5 _____ to the CD
6 _____ at the clock
7 _____ the exercise

C Pronunciation counting syllables

4 Say the words aloud and write them in the correct box.
~~question~~ Monday afternoon underline Wednesday umbrella answer evening English weekend Thursday Saturday

2 syllables	3 syllables
question	

5 **2A.1▶** Listen and check.
6 Listen again and repeat.

And you? Write the instructions in your language.

Listen and check. _____
Match the words and the pictures. _____
_____
Work with a partner. _____
Underline the correct word. _____
Ask and answer. _____

How well can you use English in the classroom now?
Go back to the Student's Book >> p.17 and tick ✓ the line again.

How to **introduce your family**

G possessive *'s*; demonstratives *this, that, these, those*   **V** family

A   Vocabulary **family**

>> The Oliver family <<

Caroline —— *Mark*

Luca   *Caitlin*

1   Tick ✓ the true sentences and correct the false sentences.

1   Luca is Mark's father.
   Luca is Mark's son   .

2   Luca is Caitlin's sister.
   _____.

3   Caroline is Mark's husband.
   _____.

4   Mark is Luca's mother.
   _____.

5   Caroline is Caitlin's mother.
   _____.

6   Luca is Caroline's husband.
   _____.

7   Mark is Luca and Caitlin's father.
   _____.

8   Caitlin is Mark's son.
   _____.

9   Caitlin and Luca are Mark and Caroline's parents.
   _____.

B   Grammar **possessive *'s*; demonstratives**

2   Introduce the Oliver family. Complete the sentences.

1   That's Mark. *His* wife*'s* name*'s* Caroline.

2   This is Luca. _____ sister _____ name _____ Caitlin.

3   That's Caroline. _____ children _____ names _____ Caitlin and Luca.

4   This is Caitlin. _____ father _____ name _____ Mark.

5   These two are Mark and Caroline. They _____ Caitlin and Luca _____ parents.

6   Those two are Caitlin and Luca. They _____ Mark and Caroline _____ children.

3   Complete the sentences with *this, that, these,* or *those.*

1   *That* 's my dog.

2   _____ are my sons.

3   _____ are my parents.

4   _____ is my daughter.

5   _____ 's my husband.

And you? Answer the questions.

What's your mother's name?
_____

What's your father's name?
_____

Are you married?
_____

How to **describe people**

G adjectives; articles *a, an*   V people; jobs   P linking words together

A Vocabulary people; jobs

1 Complete the words.

1 *g r a n d f a t h e r*
2 g _ _ _ _ m _ _ _ _ _
3 b _ _ f _ _ _ _ _
4 g _ _ _ f _ _ _ _ _
5 m _ _ _ _ _ _ c _ _ _ _
6 f _ _ _ _ _
7 t _ _ _ d _ _ _ _ _
8 o _ _ _ _ _ w _ _ _ _ _
9 f _ _ _ _ _ _ w _ _ _ _ _
10 f _ _ _ _ _ _ _ _
11 m _ _ _ _
12 a _ _ _ _ _
13 s _ _ _ _ _

B Grammar adjectives; articles *a, an*

2 Complete the phrases with *a* or *an*.

1	*a* university student	5	_____ young boy
2	_____ married couple	6	_____ school teacher
3	_____ doctor	7	_____ office worker
4	_____ engineer		

3 Complete the texts with the phrases from exercise 2.

These are friends who live in Switzerland. His name is Klaus and her name is Louise. They aren't married. She's 22 years old and she's ¹ *a university student*. He's about 30 and he's ² _____ at the local hospital.

These two are my friends from university. They're ³ _____. Their names are Annie and Paul. They have no children. He's ⁴ _____, a computer engineer, and she's ⁵ _____, a primary school teacher.

This is Françoise. She's 37 and she's divorced. She has two children: ⁶ _____ of six and a girl of sixteen. She isn't rich. She's ⁷ _____.

4 Underline the correct answers.

1 She's young woman / <u>a young woman</u>.
2 She isn't married / a married.
3 The man is a retired engineer / retired engineer.
4 He's taxi driver / a taxi driver.
5 They're a divorced couple / a couple divorced.
6 He's shop assistant / a shop assistant.
7 He isn't a rich / rich.

C Pronunciation linking words together

5 2C.1▶ Listen and draw the linking symbol.
1 His girlfriend‿is‿an‿English teacher.
2 Her parents are designers.
3 She's an engineer.
4 The shop assistant is sixteen years old.
5 My boyfriend is a good actor.

6 Listen again and repeat.

And you? Write about your friends and family.

Example My grandparents are old. They aren't rich.

My best friend _____
My boy / girlfriend _____
My husband / wife _____
My brother / sister _____
My father _____
My mother _____

How well can you describe people now?
Go back to the Student's Book ≫ p.21 and tick ✓ the line again.

How to talk about the time

G prepositions of time *at, on*   **V** numbers and time   **P** stress in corrections

A   Vocabulary   time

1   **2D.1▶** Listen and tick ✓ the time you hear.

1 a ✓   **2** a ☐   **3** a ☐

b ☐   b ☐   b ☐

4 a ☐ `8:10`   **5** a ☐ `2:40`   **6** a ☐ `5:05`

b ☐ `7:50`   b ☐ `4:20`   b ☐ `4:55`

B   Grammar   prepositions of time *at, on*

MONDAY

TV1		TV2	
8.30	News	8.45	French Class
9.00	Football Focus	9.15	Housewife of the Day
10.30	Your Doctor		
		9.45	Car Drivers

TUESDAY

TV1		TV2	
18.30	News	19.00	My Family
19.30	Celebrity Singers	19.45	News
20.30	100-question Quiz	20.00	TV Shop

2   Write *true* or *false*.

1   The football is on TV2.   *False*
2   The news is on TV1 and TV2.   _____
3   The *100-question Quiz* is on Monday evening.   _____
4   *Housewife of the Day* is on Tuesday morning.   _____
5   There is no news on TV2 on Monday morning.   _____
6   *Celebrity Singers* is on TV2 at 19.30.   _____
7   *TV Shop* is on TV2.   _____
8   *French Class* is on TV2 at 8.45.   _____

3   Complete the sentences with *at* or *on*.

1   *Football Focus* is on TV1 _on_ Monday _at_ 9.00.
2   *Celebrity Singers* is on TV1 _____ Tuesday evening _____ 19.30.
3   *French Class* is on TV2 _____ 8.45 _____ Monday.
4   *TV Shop* is on TV2 _____ 20.00 _____ Tuesday evening.
5   *Your Doctor* is on TV1 _____ Monday morning _____ 10.30.
6   *My Family* is on TV2 _____ 19.00 _____ Tuesday.
7   *Car Drivers* is _____ Tuesday _____ 9.45 on TV2.

C   Pronunciation   stress in corrections

4   **2D.2▶** Listen and <u>underline</u> the different information in the answer.

1   Is it on TV1?
No, it's on TV<u>2</u>.

2   Is it on Monday morning?
No, it's on Monday evening.

3   Is it on Tuesday morning?
No, it's on Monday morning.

4   Is it at six o'clock?
No, it's at twelve o'clock.

5   Is it at ten past eight?
No, it's at twenty past eight.

6   Is it at five to nine?
No, it's at five to ten.

7   Is it the news?
No, it's the football.

5   Listen again and copy the stress. Do you use stress like this in your language?

And you? Write the sentences in your language.

What time is it? It's half past eight.

_____

Is your class at six o'clock?

_____

It's at 11.45 on Monday morning.

_____

Unit 2 Skills Practice

A Listen for detail

1 **2S.1▶** Listen and match the messages and the places.
a ☐ office b ☐ school c ☐ shop d ☐1☐ doctor's

2 Listen again. Write the days and times in the table.

Place	Days	Times
Doctor's	*Tuesday, Thursday*	
Office		
Shop		
School		

3 Listen again and complete the information.

Doctor Watson's office ___*is*___ _____ _____
the moment. The doctor is available on Tuesday
_____ _____ _____ , from ...

4 Check the audio script on ≫ p.91.

B Listen for key words

5 **2S.2▶** Listen to Eric and number the pictures.

a ☐ b ☐

c ☐ d ☐ e ☐3☐

6 Listen again. Match the phrases with the names.

1	☐*d*☐ ☐	Eric
2	☐ ☐	Maria
3	☐ ☐	Annie & Paul
4	☐ ☐	Françoise
5	☐ ☐	Klaus & Louise

a a shop assistant
b I'm a designer
c she isn't rich
d ~~25 years old~~
e they aren't married
f primary school teacher
g not my wife
h these are friends
i a married couple
j she's divorced

7 Check the audio script on ≫ p.91.

C Read and understand

8 Read Ana's email. Put the pictures in order.

Dear Linda,

I like my new class a lot! I study with Satomi, Pablo, and Paula. Our teacher's name is Jim. We look at the pictures in the book and Jim tells us the words. Next, we repeat the words together. Then we listen to conversations on the CD. We have a conversation with our partner, and Jim listens. He tells us if we are right or wrong. It's fun to work with a partner! Sometimes we read texts from the book and write answers to the questions. If we don't understand, we ask the teacher questions, and he helps us. Do you remember our classes at school? These classes are different!

Love,

Ana

a ☐ b ☐ c ☐

d ☐1☐ e ☐

f ☐ g ☐

14

D Write **a message of introduction**

9 Do you know these famous people? Match 1–4 with the pictures.

1 This is Anastacia. She's an American singer. She's 32 years old and _____.

2 This is Sade. She's an English singer and she's 47 years old. Her father's from Nigeria. She's divorced and _____. Her daughter's name is Ila.

3 This is Ronaldinho. He's a Brazilian footballer and he's 26 years old. His girlfriend is a model – _____ _____ – and they have a young son: João.

4 This is Ben Stiller and his wife. He's 40 and he's an American actor. His wife's name is Christine. She's an actress, and _____.

10 Put these phrases in the gaps in exercise 9.

her name is Janaina
they have two children
she has a daughter
she's single

11 Order the words to make sentences about Stella McCartney. Remember full stops (.) and CAPITAL letters.

1 this stella mccartney is
2 she's designer english an
3 her a father singer is
4 she's 33 she's years married old and
5 her is alasdhair name husband's
6 they son have a baby

This is Stella McCartney. She's _____

_____

_____

_____

_____

_____

_____

_____

_____

_____

_____

_____

12 Think of ten jobs famous people do (singer, actor, etc.). Write them in your language, and write the English translation. Use your dictionary.

cantante *smf* singer

Dizionario Oxford Study per studenti d'inglese

13 Write six sentences about a famous person from your country.

This is _____.

He's / She's _____

_____

_____

_____

_____

_____

_____

14 Check your writing for full stops and capital letters.

Now try the Self check on ›› p.77.

How to ask for information

v places   P word stress

A Vocabulary places

1 Find the places in the puzzle.

T	P	R	T	O	S	U	C	E	A	C
I	L	E	X	I	T	R	H	A	I	H
C	A	S	H	M	A	C	H	I	N	E
K	T	T	I	A	T	A	X	I	O	M
E	F	A	B	O	I	R	S	T	B	I
T	O	U	O	I	O	P	T	B	U	S
O	R	R	O	O	N	A	S	R	T	T
F	M	A	K	T	I	R	T	E	R	S
F	X	N	S	S	O	K	B	X	A	B
I	C	T	H	O	A	H	A	I	I	C
C	X	T	O	I	L	E	T	S	N	F
E	S	H	P	U	B	U	A	T	R	A

2 Complete the sentences with a place from exercise 1.
1 The train is on *platform* 5.
2 Get your tickets from the _____ _____.
3 Have dinner in a _____.
4 Get a book at a _____.
5 Park your car in a _____ _____.
6 Have a drink in a _____.

3 Read the conversations. Put the words in order.
A Excuse me!
B Yes?
A are please the where toilets
  ¹ *Where are the toilets, please* ?
B Toilets?
A Yes!
B I upstairs they're think
  ² _____.
A Thank you!

A Excuse me. platform is near 5 here
  ³ _____?
B 5 is platform this
  ⁴ _____!
A Ah, thank you!

A Excuse me. Manchester this to the is bus
  ⁵ _____?
B No, it isn't. It's near the café.
A café the where's
  ⁶ _____?
B It's over there.
A Thank you!

B Pronunciation word stress

4 3A.1▶ Listen and write these words in the gaps.
chemist's   bookshop   ~~Manchester~~
telephones   platform   car park   exit
café   music shop   cash machines
1 Is this the train to *Manchester* ?
  No, that train's on _____ 4.
2 Excuse me! Where are the _____?
  They're over there, near the _____.
3 Where's the _____, please?
  It's upstairs, near the _____.
4 Excuse me, is this the _____?
  No, it isn't. It's over there, near the _____.
5 Excuse me, where are the _____, please?
  They're near the _____.

5 Listen again. Write the words in the correct box.

●•	●••
platform	Manchester

How well can you ask for information about places now?
Go back to the Student's Book >> p.27 and tick ✓ the line again.

16

How to **talk about countries**

G articles *a, an, the*   **V** countries, nationalities, languages   **P** word stress

A   **Vocabulary** countries, nationalities, languages

1 Match the countries with the flags.

1 ☑ *d* India	4 ☐ Canada	7 ☐ South Africa
2 ☐ Japan	5 ☐ Peru	8 ☐ Turkey
3 ☐ Spain	6 ☐ China	9 ☐ Brazil

2 Write the nationalities of the countries in exercise 1. Use your dictionary.

-n	-ian	-ish	-ese
Indian			

B   **Grammar** articles *a, an, the*

3 Match 1–5 with a–e.

1 ☑ *d* Hindi is an
2 ☐ New Delhi is the
3 ☐ Chennai is a
4 ☐ The rupee is the
5 ☐ India is a

a   city in India.
b   country in South Asia.
c   capital of India.
d   ~~Indian language~~.
e   currency of India.

4 <u>Underline</u> the correct word.

1 Tokyo is a / <u>the</u> capital of Japan.
2 Japanese is a / the language of Japan.
3 China is a / the country near Japan.
4 Kobe is a / the city near Osaka.
5 Japan is a / the country in Asia.
6 Japan is an / the island.

C   **Pronunciation** word stress

5 Listen and write these words in the correct box.

~~Portugal~~   Portuguese   Egypt   Egyptian
Japan   Japanese   China   Chinese

●•	•●	●••	•●•	••●
		Portugal		

6 **3B.1▶** Listen again and repeat.

How well can you talk about countries now?
Go back to the Student's Book >> p.29 and tick ✓ the line again.

17

How to say where you are in town

G plurals; prepositions of place *in*, *on*   V things and places in town   P plural endings

A Vocabulary things and places in town

1 Write these words in the correct box.

~~taxi~~ ~~woman~~ ~~house~~ church street children
supermarket lorry factory bus waiter
bike worker restaurant office driver school

places	people	transport
house	woman	taxi

2 Write five more words in the boxes. Use your dictionary.

B Grammar plurals; prepositions of place *in*, *on*

3 Write the plurals for these words.

1 city   *cities*   5 currency _____
2 country _____   6 office   _____
3 language _____   7 man   _____
4 cinema   _____   8 woman   _____

4 Write the plurals in the phrases.

1 (driver) *drivers* in their (car) *cars*
2 (person) _____ in (shop) _____
3 (family) _____ in (cinema) _____
4 (worker) _____ in (factory) _____
5 (child) _____ in (church) _____

5 Match the signs with the people in exercise 4.

a ☐   b ☐   c 1

d ☐   e ☐

6 Complete the phrases with *in* or *on*.

1 _on_ his bike

5 ____ the park

2 ____ a car

6 ____ the bus

3 ____ the table

7 ____ France

4 ____ class

8 ____ the platform

C Pronunciation plural endings

7 **3C.1▶** Listen to the singular and the plural. Write *A* or *B*.

A plural has 1 syllable	B plural has an extra syllable
car cars	page pages

1 ☐B house houses   6 ☐ glass glasses
2 ☐ school schools   7 ☐ street streets
3 ☐ watch watches   8 ☐ girl girls
4 ☐ shop shops   9 ☐ town towns
5 ☐ church churches

8 Listen again and repeat.

> **And you?** Write the names of two places in your town.
>
> 1 Two restaurants: _____ _____
> 2 Two shops: _____ _____
> 3 Two schools: _____ _____

How well can you say where you are in town now?
Go back to the Student's Book >> p.31 and tick ✓ the line again.

How to talk about language skills

G present simple ⊞⊟⊡ *do, don't*   V phrases describing language ability   P *Sue* /s/ or *shoe* /ʃ/

A Grammar present simple ⊞-⊡? *do, don't*

1 Complete the conversation with *do* or *don't*.

A ¹ *Do* you speak English?

B No, I ²_____.

A ³_____ you understand English?

B Yes, I ⁴_____. I understand a little.

A ⁵_____ you read English?

B No, I ⁶_____.

A ⁷_____ you write English?

B Yes, I ⁸_____. I write a little.

A ⁹_____ you like English?

B I ¹⁰_____ know!

B Vocabulary phrases describing language ability

2 Jon is a student in a Chinese class. Underline the correct words.

1 I read Chinese quite well / quite well Chinese.

2 I write a little Chinese / Chinese a little.

3 I understand very well Chinese / Chinese very well.

4 I don't speak Chinese very well / very well Chinese.

5 I pronounce quite well Chinese / Chinese quite well.

6 I know a little vocabulary / vocabulary a little.

3 Chen and Jun are students in a German class. Write their sentences.

1 read / quite well

We read German quite well _____.

2 write / not very well

_____.

3 understand / very well

_____.

4 speak / a little

_____.

5 pronounce / not very well

_____.

C Pronunciation *Sue* /s/ or *shoe* /ʃ/

4 Is the underlined sound /s/ or /ʃ/? Say these words aloud and write them in the correct box.

Russian   France   ~~Spanish~~   South African   Swedish   Swahili   nationality   currency   Egyptian   Polish

/s/	/ʃ/
Spanish	*Spanish*

5 Check your answers in your dictionary. Practise saying the words.

And you? Write three sentences about your English.

Example I speak English quite well.

_____

_____

_____

Unit 3 Skills Practice

A Listen for key information

1 **3S.1▶** Listen to five conversations. Tick ✓ the places you hear.

- ☐ toilets
- ☐ chemist's
- ☐ South Street exit
- ☐ bus stop
- ☐ café
- ☐ cash machines

2 Listen again and write the places in the gaps.

Back Street Shopping Centre

A1	car park exit	**A8**	4_____
A2	1_____	**A9**	supermarket
A3	emergency exit	**A10**	café
A4	taxis	**A11**	music shop
A5	2_____	**A12**	pub
A6	bookshop	**A13**	public phones
A7	3_____	**A14**	5_____

OPENING HOURS Monday–Saturday: 9.00 a.m.–6.00 p.m.
Sunday: 10.00 a.m.–5.00 p.m.

3 Listen again. Put the words in order.

1 a here is stop there bus near
*Is there a bus stop near here*_____?

2 the look cash machines there are
_____.

3 I have me don't my with glasses
_____.

4 shopping at centre other of the end the
_____.

5 it oh is yes here
_____!

4 Check the audio script on ≫ p.91.

B Read and understand messages

5 Is the information correct? Look at the map and write *true* or *false*.

1 The taxis are near the South Street exit. *False*_____

2 The taxis are near the bookshop. _____

3 The toilets are near the chemist's. _____

4 There are phones in the supermarket. _____

5 The pub is near the music shop. _____

6 There are no cash machines at the car park exit. _____

7 On Tuesdays, the centre is closed. _____

8 The centre is open on Sundays. _____

6 Where are they? Match the text messages with the letters a–e on the map.

1 *c* I'm at the bus stop in the street.

2 ☐ I'm in the pub, near the public phones.

3 ☐ I'm at the chemist's, near the toilets.

4 ☐ We're at the South Street exit, near the supermarket.

5 ☐ I'm in the café, near the music shop.

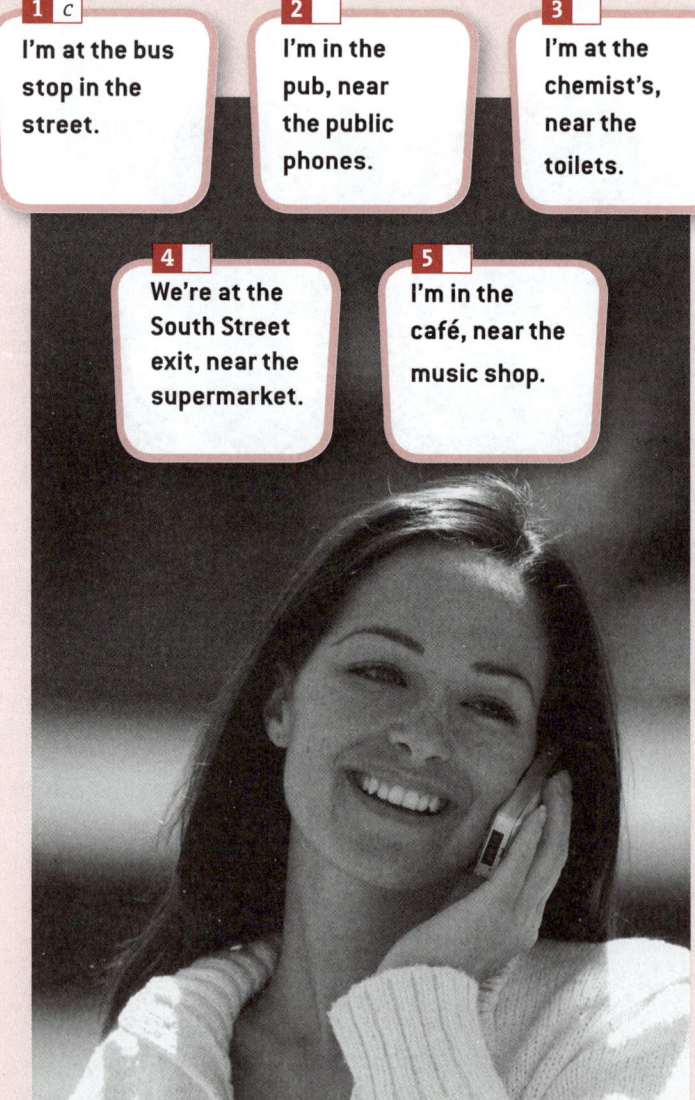

20

C Read for key information

7 Match the hotels and the guests.

1 A family with three young children and a dog. They travel by train.
2 A middle-aged couple. They are in a car, and want to walk around the city.
3 A young couple. The want to go out in the evening and dance.

a

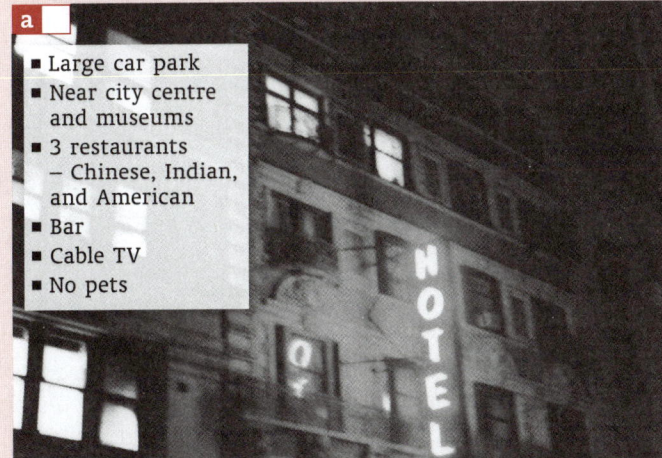

- Large car park
- Near city centre and museums
- 3 restaurants – Chinese, Indian, and American
- Bar
- Cable TV
- No pets

b

- Five-minute walk to station
- Swimming pool
- Family rooms
- TV and telephone in every room
- No smoking
- Pets welcome

c

- Car park
- Near pubs, nightclubs, and cinema
- Restaurant
- Cable TV
- Bar

8 Underline three or four words you don't know. Use your dictionary to look up their meaning.

D Write quiz questions

9 Make a list of ten countries. Write the nationalities. Use your dictionary.

country	nationality
Scotland	Scottish

10 Complete the text with these words.

what's   currency   nationality   ~~flag~~   language

This is the Scottish ¹ _flag_____. The ² _____
of Scotland is the pound. The ³ _____ is
English and the ⁴ _____ is Scottish.
But ⁵ _____ the capital of Scotland?

a London   b Cardiff   c Edinburgh

11 Correct the text. Add CAPITAL letters.

T̸his is the argentinian flag. the capital of argentina is

buenos aires and the language is spanish. but what's the

currency of argentina?

a euro   b peso   c dollar

12 Write a quiz question about another country. Write three or four sentences.

_This is the _____ flag._ _____

_____

_____

_____

13 Check your sentences for capital letters.

Now try the Self check on >> p.78.

How to **respond to news**

G prepositions of place *at*   **V** signs; responses to news   **P** responses to news

A Vocabulary signs

1 Find the eleven signs and write them below.

closed **half-price** sold out open sorry we're full please help yourself no vacancies private cancelled free entry out of order

half-price – supermarket

_____   _____

_____   _____

_____   _____

_____   _____

_____

_____

2 Where can you see the signs? Write a different place for each sign.

3 Complete the sentences with some of the signs from exercise 1.

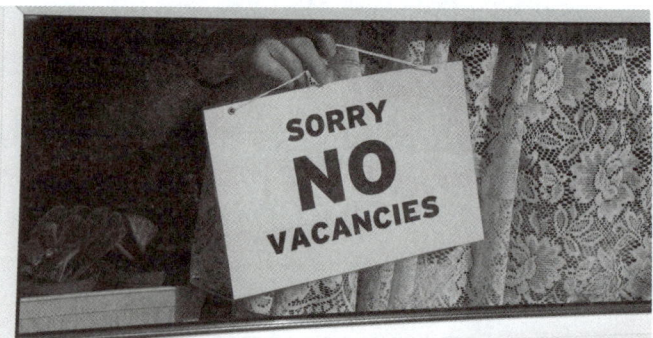

1 A Do you have a room for tonight, please?

 B I'm sorry, we have *no vacancies* for tonight.

2 A Is it €5 for the cinema tomorrow night?

 B No, €2.50! It's _____ on Sunday nights!

3 Flight BD332 is _____ because of bad weather.

4 A Do you have your ticket?

 B No, the machine is _____ _____ _____!

5 I'm sorry, the office is _____ now.
We are _____ on Monday at nine o'clock.

6 A Is that the toilet?

 B No, the sign on the door says '_____
– no entry'.

B Vocabulary responses to news

4 Match 1–10 with a–j.

1 [c] The football's on in five minutes but
2 ☐ I'm at the supermarket and
3 ☐ My car! My car!
4 ☐ We have a
5 ☐ My sister has
6 ☐ We get married
7 ☐ My father's
8 ☐ My cat
9 ☐ School is
10 ☐ It's 9.30

a everything is half-price today. I'm sorry! / That's great!
b new car! Oh no! / Oh really?
c ~~the TV is out of order~~. Good luck! / <u>Oh no!</u>
d It's not in the car park! Oh no! / Good luck!
e a new baby. That's great! / I'm sorry!
f and my exam's at ten o'clock. Good luck! / Well done!
g on Monday! I'm sorry! / Good luck!
h closed today. Well done! / That's great!
i isn't very well. That's great! / I'm sorry!
j in bed. Oh really? / Well done!

5 <u>Underline</u> the best response for the news in exercise 4.

C Pronunciation responses to news

6 **4A.1▶** Listen and check your answers. Copy the pronunciation of the responses.

And you? Write your good news and your bad news.
1
2
3
4

22

How to **say dates**

A Vocabulary **months and ordinal numbers**

1 Follow the instructions and complete the puzzle.
1 Write the last letter of the first month.
2 Write the third letter of the third month.
3 Write the first letter of the fourth month.
4 Write the second letter of the seventh month.
5 Write the last letter of the ninth month.
6 Write the sixth letter of the twelfth month.
7 Write the fourth letter of the sixth month.
8 Write the first letter of the second month.

Y

↑

9 Find the month in the letters. _____

B Pronunciation /θ/

2 **4B.1▶** Listen and write the dates.
1 *the seventh of April* _____ 4 _____
2 _____ 5 _____
3 _____ 6 _____

3 Listen again and repeat. Practise the /θ/ sound.

C Grammar **prepositions of time *at, in, on***

May

19	
20	
21	1.15 Dentist
22	
23	
24	Doctor 9.30
25	
26	
27	Theatre 20.30
28	
29	
30	
31	21.00 Cinema

June

1	
2	
3	Party! 20.00
4	
5	Train to Berlin 22.00
6	
7	
8	Birthday – restaurant 19.30
9	
10	16.30 German exam
11	

4 Complete the sentences with *at, in,* or *on.*
1 When's the cinema? It's _on_ May 31st _at_ 9 p.m.
2 And the theatre? That's ____ May 27th ____ 8.30 ____ the evening.
3 When's the restaurant? That's ____ June, ____ the 8th, ____ 7.30 p.m.
4 And the doctor? It's ____ 9.30 ____ May 24th.
5 And the dentist? It's ____ May 21st ____ 1.15.
6 Oh, and my German exam? It's ____ 4.30 ____ the afternoon ____ June 10th.
7 And the train to Berlin? That's ____ June, ____ the 5th, ____ 10 p.m.
8 When's the party? It's ____ 8 p.m. ____ June 3rd.

5 Order the words to make questions.
A birthday is your date what
1 _____?
B It's on February 12th.
A time English what your class is
2 _____?
B It's at 10.30.
A shopping day you what go do
3 _____?
B On Fridays.
A holidays your when are summer
4 _____?
B They're in August.

And you? Answer the questions in exercise 5.
1
2
3
4

How well can you say dates now?
Go back to the Student's Book >> p.39 and tick ✓ the line again.

23

How to describe habits

G present simple with *he / she / it*   **V** morning habits   **P** final *-s*

A Vocabulary morning habits

1 Write these phrases in the correct box.

~~to work~~ breakfast back to bed up for a run
to the kitchen a shower dressed tea or coffee

go	get	have
to work		

B Grammar present simple with *he / she / it*

2 Read the text and put the pictures in order.

Tom ¹ *is*_____ a bit different. He works in a factory, not
in an office, and he works at night. He ²_____ work
at nine in the evening and ³_____ at five in the
morning. When he gets home, he ⁴_____ a shower
and ⁵_____ to bed. At about eleven o'clock, he gets
up and has breakfast: coffee and toast. After breakfast he
⁶_____ the newspaper or ⁷_____ to the news
on the radio. Then he ⁸_____ tennis with friends, or
sometimes he ⁹_____ languages. His new language
is Italian – it's his third foreign language. At the
weekend he gets up late and ¹⁰_____ TV.

3 Complete the text with these verbs in the correct form.

~~be~~ go watch finish study play have
read start listen

4 Write the complete questions.

1 Where / work *Where does he work*_____? In a factory.
2 When / finish work _____?
   At five in the morning.
3 What time / get up _____?
   About eleven o'clock.
4 What / have for breakfast _____?
   Coffee and toast.
5 What / do after breakfast _____?
   He reads the newspaper.
6 play football _____? No, he doesn't.
7 When / get up late _____?
   At the weekend.

C Pronunciation final *-s*

5 Complete the lines with these words and phrases.

TV the house late for a run the mail
her teeth ~~early~~ work fruit for breakfast

1 He wakes up   *early*_____
2 She gets up   _____
3 He checks   _____
4 She goes   _____
5 He has   _____
6 She leaves   _____
7 He watches   _____
8 She brushes   _____
9 He finishes   _____

6 **4C.1▶** Listen and check.

7 Listen again and repeat. Copy the pronunciation.

And you? Answer the questions.

Where do you work / study?
_____

What time do you get up in the morning?
_____

Do you have a big breakfast?
_____

When do you leave home?
_____

How well can you describe morning habits now?
Go back to the Student's Book >> p.41 and tick ✓ the line again.

How to **describe a typical day**

G adverbs of frequency   **P** *leave* /iː/ or *live* /ɪ/

A **Grammar** **adverbs of frequency**

1 Match the two parts of the actions.

late for work   a coffee break   the boss   the clock
~~to work~~   home   the newspaper   some letters   lunch

1 drive *to work*   2 arrive _____   3 read _____

4 have _____   5 write _____   6 have _____

7 listen to _____   8 look at _____   9 drive _____

2 Write the sentences with the adverbs in brackets.

1 He drives to work. (always) *He always drives to work.*

2 He arrives early for work. (not often)
   He doesn't often arrive early for work   .

3 He reads the newspaper. (often)

   _____ .

4 He's late for his coffee break. (never)

   _____ .

5 He writes letters. (sometimes)

   _____ .

6 He has lunch for two hours. (often)

   _____ .

7 He listens to the boss. (not usually)

   _____ .

8 He looks at the clock. (always)

   _____ .

9 He's the first to leave work. (always)

   _____ .

3 Order the words to make questions.

A job   like   your   you   do
¹ *Do you like your job*   ?

B It's OK.

A when   holiday   you   on   go   do
²_____?

B Usually in August, sometimes in December.

A usually   you   go   do   where
³_____?

B To the beach or to another country.

A friends   family   with   you   or   go   do
⁴_____?

B With friends.

A holiday   car   the   you   do   on   use
⁵_____?

B Yes, always.

B **Pronunciation** *leave* /iː/ or *live* /ɪ/

4 **4D.1▶** Say these words aloud and write them in the correct box.

~~this~~   mean   sleep   people   listen   finish   repeat
thing   three

leave /iː/	live /ɪ/
	this

5 Check your answers in your dictionary. Practise saying the words.

And you? Answer the questions in exercise 3.
1
2
3
4
5

Unit 4 Skills Practice

A Read and understand

1 Match the pictures with the paragraphs.

a Selina is a ten-year-old girl who lives with her brothers and sisters, her parents, grandmother, and uncle and aunt. The family live in a small village in Ethiopia and they have breakfast together early in the morning, at about six o'clock.

b At seven o'clock, after breakfast, the adults leave the village. The men work in the fields, and the women get water and firewood.

c Selina and one of her sisters clean the house, wash the dishes, and take the small children to another aunt's house.

d At eight o'clock, Selina goes to school. She is the only person in the family who goes to school. The children often have classes outside, in the shade of a big tree.

e At half-past twelve, the children go home to have lunch. Selina usually has an hour to do her homework before she goes back to school in the afternoon. Afternoon classes are from half-past two to five.

f The family come back home after work late in the afternoon, about half-past six. They have dinner near the fire. After dinner, the small children often play together, the schoolchildren do their homework and the adults have conversations with their friends. They usually go to bed at about half-past nine.

2 Underline three or four words you don't know. Guess their meaning, and then check in your dictionary.

B Listen for key words

3 **4S.1▶** Listen and underline the countries you hear.

Austria
England
France
Germany
Holland
Italy
Poland

4 Listen and match the days and the countries.

1 ☑ d Monday   a Italy
2 ☐ Tuesday   b Germany
3 ☐ Wednesday   c France
4 ☐ Thursday   d Holland
5 ☐ Friday   e Austria
6 ☐ Saturday and Sunday

5 Listen to the beginning of the interview again. Complete the text.

A So, Jack, you're a lorry driver. Tell me _about_ _____ normal week.

J Normal week? _____ _____ _____ any normal weeks! Yeah, well, I usually work _____ _____ _____, but, erm, it's often _____ too.

6 Check the audio script on >> p.92.

C Read for detail

7 Read Ana's email and complete the table.

> Hello Giselle!
>
> How are you? I'm really looking forward to your visit. I'm very busy, so I don't have much time to see you. I work three mornings a week from eight till two, that's Monday, Wednesday, and Friday, and the other two days I work in the afternoon and evening, from three till nine o'clock. I always have lunch at two o'clock, even on Saturdays. I normally go shopping on Thursday mornings. On Monday and Friday afternoons I often go to the gym to get some exercise, usually at about five o'clock. Oh, and I have my French class on Tuesday mornings. In the evenings I like to stay at home, but on Friday and Saturday evenings I go out with my friends. And Saturday is my day for getting up late. I have breakfast about half-past ten on Saturday mornings. Maybe Sunday is the best day to come!
>
> Write back soon!
>
> Love,
>
> Ana

Monday	8.00–2.00 work	2.00 lunch	5.00 _____	
Tuesday	9.00–11.00 _____	2.00 _____	3.00–9.00 _____	
Wednesday	8.00–2.00 work	2.00 _____		
Thursday	9.30–11.30 _____	2.00 lunch	3.00–9.00 _____	
Friday	8.00–2.00 work	2.00 lunch	5.00 _____	evening _____
Saturday	10.30 _____	2.00 _____		evening _____

8 Write *true* or *false*.

1 Ana doesn't work at the weekend. _____*True*_____

2 She doesn't have lunch on Tuesdays. _____

3 She goes shopping one day a week. _____

4 She goes to the gym on Mondays. _____

5 She studies French on Tuesdays. _____

6 She goes out every night. _____

7 On Saturday mornings she has breakfast very early. _____

D Write about your day

9 Read part of Giselle's email. Find and correct eight more spelling mistakes.

>   *usually*
> ...I ~~ussually~~ go shoping on
> Teusdays, when most poeple
> are at work. My favourite day
> is Wensday too. That's when I
> often go out on my byke. Two
> days a week I go to a driving
> school. My fahter can't drive
> now, so I have driving lesons
> to help my famly...

10 Complete the sentences about your day.

I always _____
_____ .

I often _____
_____ .

I don't often _____
_____ .

I usually _____
_____ .

I sometimes _____
_____ .

I never _____
_____ .

11 Check your writing for spelling mistakes.

Now try the Self check on >> p.79.

How to **introduce people**

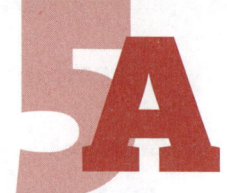

G object pronouns; prepositions of place *next to, opposite* **V** phrases to introduce people **P** vowels

A **Vocabulary** phrases to introduce people

1 Order the words to make sentences and questions.

1 me you remember do __*Do you remember me*__ ?
2 boyfriend know my you do

_____ ?

3 what's again sorry name your

_____ ?

4 I'm sorry but your name don't I remember

_____ .

5 and them meet come

_____ .

B **Grammar** object pronouns

2 Complete the sentences with these words.

~~you~~ us them it him her me

1 I know __*you*__, but you don't know _____.

2 She likes _____, but he doesn't like _____.

3 We know _____, but they don't know _____.

4 The dog likes the children, but they don't like _____.

3 Complete the conversation about the people in the picture.

Bill   Who's that? I don't know ¹ __*him*__ .
Maggie That's Dick. ² _____ works in my office. He sits next to me.
B   And who's that woman next to ³ _____? I don't know ⁴ _____.
M   That's Maya. I think she's Dick's girlfriend.
B   And that couple over there? Who are ⁵ _____?
M   Don't ask ⁶ _____! I don't know ⁷ _____!
B   Look! There's Cathy.
M   I don't remember ⁸ _____.
B   Don't you? ⁹ _____ lives near us, opposite the newspaper shop.
M   Oh, yes.
B   Coffee?
M   No, thanks. I don't really like ¹⁰ _____.

C **Pronunciation** vowels *a, e, i, o, u*

4 Match the vowel with the pronunciation. Use your dictionary.

a e i o u

/əʊ/ ____ /iː/ ____ /eɪ/ _*a*_ /aɪ/ ____ /juː/ ____

5 Which words have the same vowel sound? Match the words with the letter.

~~day~~ ~~tea~~ ~~buy~~ ~~go~~ ~~you~~ rule three know two five blue eight nine speak school drive say play name show like meet

a _*day*_ _____
e _*tea*_ _____
i _*buy*_ _____
o _*go*_ _____
u _*you*_ _____

6 Check your answers in your dictionary.

How well can you introduce people now?
Go back to the Student's Book >> p.47 and tick ✓ the line again.

How to **describe people and objects**

G order of adjectives   V adjectives   P *man* /æ/ or *men* /e/

A   **Vocabulary** adjectives

1   Write the opposites.

fat cat

thin cat

black cat

_____

old bike

_____

big bike

_____

tall tree

_____

old clock

_____

long street

_____

fat book

_____

short hair

_____

B   **Grammar** order of adjectives

2   Put the words in the correct order.

1	taxi	a	black	big	*a big black taxi*
2	old	buses	grey	two	_____
3	grey	offices	tall		_____
4	big	a	factory	new	_____
5	tall	four	trees	green	_____
6	bike	a	white	new	_____
7	fat	two	cats	white	_____
8	man	a	blond	short	_____
9	a	black	umbrella	big	_____

3   Match the phrases in exercise 2 with some of the things in the picture.

C   **Pronunciation** *man* /æ/ or *men* /e/

4   Say these words aloud and write them in the correct box.

~~get~~ ~~bag~~ have cat spell bank text guess
fact very friend bad a<u>gain</u>

/æ/ man	/e/ men
bag	*get*

5   Check your answers in your dictionary. Practise saying the words.

> **And you?** Complete the sentences.
>
> In my home, I've got a new _____ and a big _____. I've also got
> an old _____, a black _____ and a white _____. I haven't
> got a fat _____ or a tall _____.

How well can you describe people and objects now?
Go back to the Student's Book >> p.49 and tick ✓ the line again.

How to **ask for things in shops**

G *have got* **V** office supplies; shopping phrases

A Vocabulary office supplies

1 Complete the crossword.

Across

Down

B Grammar *I / you / we / they have got*

2 Complete the sentences with the correct form of *have*.

1 We'*ve* got two sons, but we _____ got a daughter.

2 _____ you got a car?
No, I _____ .

3 _____ they got any children?
Yes, they _____ . They'_____ got a daughter.

4 I'_____ got a computer, but I _____ got a printer.

3 Put the words in order to make the questions and answers.

1 car you a got have
Have you got a car _____ ?
No, motorbike a got I've
_____ .

2 children any got you have
_____ ?
Yes, two boy girls got and we've a
_____ .

3 got any they pets have
_____ ?
Yes, a two got cats they've and mouse
_____ .

C Vocabulary shopping phrases

4 Match the questions and answers.

1 [c] Have you got any colour ink?
2 [ ] Excuse me, can you help me?
3 [ ] Black or colour?
4 [ ] Anything else?
5 [ ] How much is that?

a That's all, thanks.
b Twenty-seven euros.
c ~~No, I'm sorry, we haven't~~.
d Colour, please.
e Yes, of course.

And you? Write these phrases in your language.

Can I help you? _____ ?

Here you are. _____ .

That's all, thanks. _____ .

How well can you ask for things in a shop now?
Go back to the Student's Book >> p.51 and tick ✓ the line again.

How to **ask about people's interests**

G *has got* V gifts P stress timing

A Grammar *he / she / it has got*

1 Match the questions and answers.

1 ☑ *d* Have you got a watch?
2 ☐ What has she got in her bag?
3 ☐ Has the hotel got a car park?
4 ☐ Does she cook?
5 ☐ Has he got any pets?
6 ☐ What colour eyes has he got?
7 ☐ Does he like animals?
8 ☐ Has she got a car?

a A pen, a pencil, and a notebook.
b Yes, he has. A dog.
c Sometimes!
d ~~Yes, I have.~~
e Blue.
f I'm sorry, it hasn't.
g No, she doesn't drive.
h Yes, he does.

2 Look at the pictures and write ten differences.

1 *She's got an old computer but he's got a new one* _____.
2 _____.
3 _____.
4 _____.
5 _____.
6 _____.
7 _____.
8 _____.
9 _____.
10 _____.

B Pronunciation **stress timing**

3 Complete the sentences with these words.

nice ~~car~~ house dog watch

1 I've **got** a **bike** but I **ha**ven't got a _car_ .
2 I've **got** a **clock** but I **want** to get a _____.
3 I've **got** a **cat** but I'd **ra**ther have a _____.
4 I've **got** a **flat** but I **want** to buy a _____.
5 I've **got** a **wife** but she **is**n't very _____. Sorry, dear.

4 **5D.1▶** Listen and check. Copy the stress.

And you? Describe your room.

Example My room's got a bed, a cupboard, and two chairs.

My room _____. It hasn't got
_____. It's got _____
_____ and _____.

A Read and understand

1 Read the puzzle and complete the chart.

The Smith family live at Number 1, and they've got two children. The family in the house opposite them have one teenage child. This teenager hasn't got any pets. Her boyfriend lives at Number 5.

The Jones family live at the other end of the street, at Number 6. They haven't got any children, but they've got pets: two cats and a dog. The Molina family live next to the Joneses. They've got two children, who play with the three children in the house opposite. The Molina children also play with their pet rabbit.

The Patel family live next to the Smiths. They've got two dogs. The dogs don't like the Smiths' grey cat. The Kowalski family live opposite the Joneses. They've got one teenage child and three cats.

The family opposite the Smiths are the Dixons, and they've got a big black car. Their neighbours at Number 4 have got a big grey car, but the neighbours at Number 6 haven't got a car. They've got a motorbike. The boy in the house opposite would like to ride that motorbike. His parents have got an old blue car.

The family opposite the Molinas have got two cars, one for the husband and one for the wife. Their neighbours at Number 1 have got a red car.

Nº 1
family *Smith*
children _____
transport _____
pets _____

Nº 3
family _____
children _____
transport _____
pets _____

Nº 5
family _____
children *1 boy*
transport _____
pets _____

Nº 2
family _____
children _____
transport *black car*
pets _____

Nº 4
family _____
children _____
transport _____
pets *rabbit*

Nº 6
family *Jones*
children _____
transport _____
pets _____

B Listen for key phrases

2 **5S.1▶** Listen to people meeting. Tick ✓ the number of speakers.
a ☐1 ☐2 ☐3 ☐4
b ☐1 ☐2 ☐3 ☐4
c ☐1 ☐2 ☐3 ☐4

3 Match the conversations with the people.
☐ Jenny meets Ricardo and Elena.
☐ Stella meets Sheila.
☐ Henry meets Mr Patel.

4 Listen again. Match the conversations with the phrases.
1 ☐ Come and meet her.
2 ☐ Come and meet him.
3 ☐ Do you remember me?
4 ☐ This is my wife.
5 ☐a Do you know my brother?
6 ☐ Sorry, what's your name again?

5 Read and listen to the first conversation again. Correct five more mistakes.
A Mr Patel! ~~Who~~ *How* are you?
B Fine, thanks, Mike. And you?
A I'm fine, thank you. Do you know my brother Henry?
B No, I don't think so.
A Come and meet her. Henry, this is Mr Patel, your neighbour. Mr Patel, Henry, my father.
C Nice to meet you!
B Yes, me too.

6 Check the audio script on ≫ p.92.

C Read for detail

7 Match the descriptions and the pictures.

> **1** She's got big blue eyes and short brown hair. She lives in the flat next door and she works in the local hairdresser's. She often goes to an Indian restaurant, and she likes green tea. She's got a little brown dog that she takes for a walk every afternoon. She reads fashion magazines and listens to techno music at the weekend.

> **2** She's got blue eyes and short hair. She works in the hairdresser's and likes Chinese food, but she doesn't go out very often. She listens to pop music and reads the newspaper every day. She's got a big dog, and she takes it to the park every morning.

> **3** She's got brown eyes and long blond hair. She lives in the flat next door and she's a student at the local university. She doesn't like dogs, but she's got a small white cat called Boris. She usually buys a newspaper and reads it in a café with a cup of coffee.

a ☐   **b** ☐

c ☐

8 Find these words in the texts.

1 a word that means *Saturday and Sunday*   <u>weekend</u>

2 the opposite of *short*   _____

3 a word that means the same as *small*   _____

4 a place with trees and grass   _____

5 two animals   _____   _____

6 two nationalities   _____   _____

7 two types of music   _____   _____

8 two drinks   _____   _____

9 five colours   _____

D Write a description

9 Put apostrophes (') in the text.

He's short and bald, but hes got lovely blue eyes. He works in an office and he loves Italian food. He drinks red wine every weekend. He doesnt watch much TV, but he likes a good film. His names Henry – hes my dad and hes OK.

10 Think of ten adjectives in your language to describe people. Write the adjectives and the English translation. Use your dictionary.

> **simpático, -a** *adj* ⟨nice:⟩ *Es una chica muy simpática.* She's a very nice girl. ◊ *Me pareció/cayó muy ~.* I thought he was very nice.

Diccionario Oxford Pocket para estudiantes de inglés

adjective	English

11 Write a description of a friend or someone in your family. Write five sentences.

_____

_____

_____

_____

_____

12 Check your sentences for apostrophes. Do you use apostrophes in the same way in your language?

Now try the Self check on >> p.80.

How to **ask about prices**

G countable and uncountable   **V** food and drink; prices   **P** sentence stress

A **Vocabulary** food and drink

1 Complete the crossword.

Across

3   8   11

6   9   12

11 ``c h o c o l a t e s``

Down

1   4   7

2   5   10

B **Grammar** countable and uncountable

2 Write the words from the crossword in the correct box.

countable	uncountable
chocolates	

3 Add these words to the table in exercise 2.

pens   perfume   newspapers   CDs   paper
ink   batteries   pencils

4 Complete the questions with *is* or *are*.

1 How much _is_____ the wine?
2 How much _____ the oranges?
3 How much _____ the coffee?
4 How much _____ the newspaper?
5 How much _____ the pens?
6 How much _____ the milk?
7 How much _____ the chocolates?

5 Put the conversation in order.
A ☐1 How much are the biscuits, please?
A ☐ Here you are.
A ☐ OK. I'd like two cups of coffee and two packets of biscuits.
A ☐ How much is the coffee?

B ☐ Thank you.
B ☐ That's €4.60, please.
B ☐ It's €1.30.
B ☐ They're €1 a packet.

C **Pronunciation** sentence stress

6 **6A.1**▶ Listen and underline the stressed words.
How much are the crisps?
How much is the wine?
They're one euro twenty,
and five ninety-nine.

7 Check the audio script on >> p.92. Listen again and copy the stress.

How well can you ask about prices now?
Go back to the Student's Book >> p.57 and tick ✓ the line again.

How to **order food in a café**

G *some, any* **V** food **P** spellings *ee* and *ea*

A **Vocabulary food**

applechocolatebreadchickensandwich
tomatosausagefish

1 Find the eight words and write them below.

1 f *ish*_____ and chips   5 c_____ legs
2 b_____ and jam   6 a_____ pie
3 s_____ and eggs   7 t_____ salad
4 toasted s_____   8 c_____ cake

2 Write the phrases from exercise 1 in the gaps.

Dave's café

Fish	**Vegetables**

Meat	**Others**	
steak and chips	pizza	
_____	_____	_____
_____	_____	_____

Drinks	
tea	coffee

B **Grammar *some, any***

3 Write sentences about the picture.

1 meat   *We've got some meat*_____.
2 eggs   *We haven't got any eggs*_____.
3 fish   _____.
4 tomatoes _____.
5 milk   _____.
6 cake   _____.
7 carrots   _____.
8 sausages _____.

4 Complete the conversation with these words.

any ~~can~~ like some have please don't would

A ¹*Can*_____ I help you?
B I'd ²_____ some chicken legs with tomato salad.
A Sorry, we haven't got ³_____ chicken today – but we've got ⁴_____ tomato salad.
B Well, can I ⁵_____ some fish?
A With chips?
B No, thank you. I ⁶_____ like chips.
A OK, that's fish with tomato salad. ⁷_____ you like anything to drink?
B Just a cup of tea, ⁸_____.
A Thank you!

C **Pronunciation spellings *ee* and *ea***

5 Say these words aloud and write them in the correct box.

~~tree~~ ~~break~~ week speak peas bread cheese three steak tea beans please great

/iː/	other sounds
tree	break

6 Check your answers in your dictionary. Practise saying the words.

And you? Think about your next shopping trip. What do you need?
1 *We don't need any milk.*
2
3
4
5
6

How well can you order food in a café now?
Go back to the Student's Book >> p.59 and tick ✓ the line again.

How to **talk about food**

G *there is, there are* **V** food **P** *-er* = /ə/

A Vocabulary food

1 Complete the words.

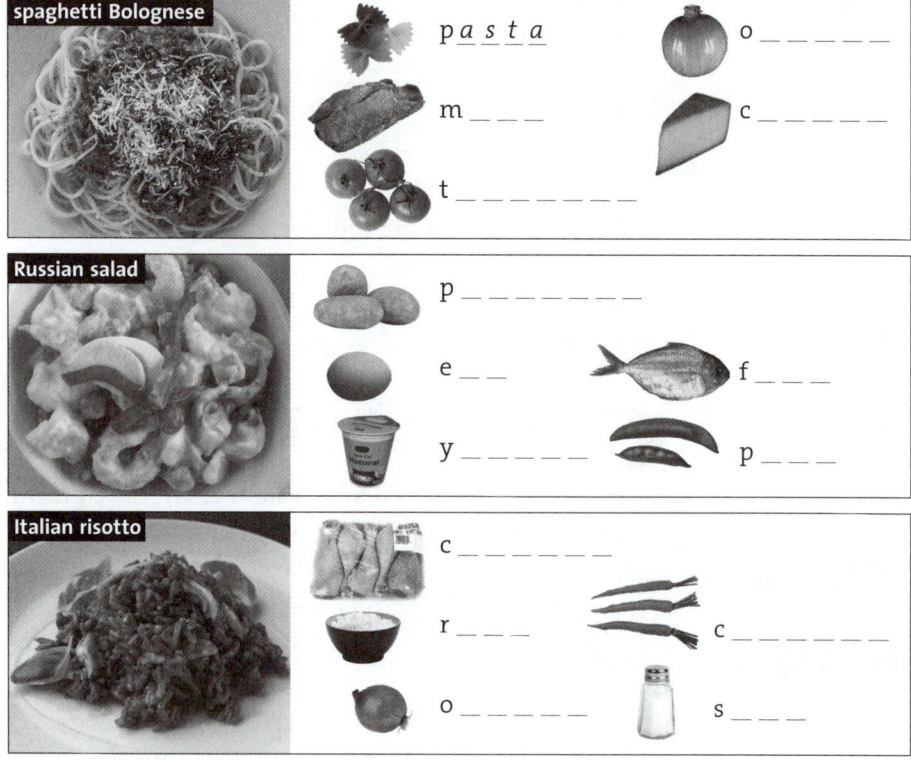

spaghetti Bolognese

p _a_ _s_ _t_ _a_
m _ _ _ _
t _ _ _ _ _ _ _ _
o _ _ _ _ _ _
c _ _ _ _ _ _

Russian salad

p _ _ _ _ _ _ _
e _ _
y _ _ _ _ _ _
f _ _ _
p _ _ _

Italian risotto

c _ _ _ _ _ _ _
r _ _ _ _
o _ _ _ _ _ _
c _ _ _ _ _ _ _
s _ _ _

B Grammar *there is, there are*

A

B

2 Write sentences about the differences.

1 *In A there's some rice, but there isn't any pasta* .
2 *In B there aren't any oranges* .
3 _____ .
4 _____ .
5 _____ .
6 _____ .
7 _____ .
8 _____ .

3 Write questions with the word in brackets. Look at picture *b* and write the answers.

1 (onions) *Are there any onions?* ___
   Yes, there are. _____
2 (eggs) _____ ?
   _____ .
3 (yogurt) _____ ?
   _____ .
4 (rice) _____ ?
   _____ .
5 (apples) _____ ?
   _____ .
6 (sugar) _____ ?
   _____ .

C Pronunciation *-er* = /ə/

4 Underline all the words ending in *-er* and *-or*.

My sister likes an actor,
so she buys him a flower,
she sends him a letter,
but he never sends an answer.

5 **6C.1▶** Listen and repeat. Practise the /ə/ sound.

And you? What do you need to make your favourite meals? Write the ingredients. Use your dictionary if necessary.

_____
_____
_____
_____
_____
_____

How well can you talk about food now?
Go back to the Student's Book >> p.61 and tick ✓ the line again.

How to **offer things**

A Grammar *much, many, a lot of*

1 Complete the sentences. Use *much, many,* or *a lot of.*

1 There *isn't much* _____ butter.
2 There _____ milk.
3 There _____ eggs.
4 There _____ bread.
5 There _____ apples.
6 There _____ coffee.
7 There _____ carrots.
8 There _____ cakes.

2 Write the questions.

1 butter *How much butter is there* _____ ?
2 milk _____ ?
3 eggs _____ ?
4 bread _____ ?
5 apples _____ ?
6 coffee _____ ?
7 carrots _____ ?
8 cakes _____ ?

B Vocabulary **offering phrases**

3 Order the words to make questions.

A coffee cup like you of would a
1 _____ ?

B Yes, please.
A milk take sugar you and do
2 _____ ?

B Just sugar, thanks.
A toast like any you would
3 _____ ?

B Yes, please.
A or want jam butter you do
4 _____ ?

B Butter is fine, thanks.
A Try these cakes – they're delicious!
B Sorry, I don't really like cakes.

C Pronunciation **unstressed words** *a, of, some, and, with, or*

4 Complete the phrases with these words.

like ~~butter~~ eggs water sugar pizza legs coffee

some	**bread**	and	*butter* _____
some	**ham**	and	_____
a	**piece**	of	_____
some	**chi**	cken	_____
some	**tea**	or	_____
with	**milk**	or	_____
What	would	you	_____ ?
a	**glass**	of	_____

... please!

5 **6D.1▶** Listen and check.

6 Listen again and notice the unstressed words. Copy the pronunciation.

A Read for detail

1 Match the words with the examples.

1 [a] meal   a ~~breakfast, lunch, dinner~~
2 ☐ course   b apples, oranges
3 ☐ fruit   c chicken, steak
4 ☐ vegetables   d first, second, dessert
5 ☐ meat   e peas, carrots, onions

2 Read about six restaurants and answer the questions.

1 Which restaurant closes on Mondays? _4_
2 Which restaurant offers half-price food? _____
3 Which restaurants are in the same street? _____
    and _____
4 Which restaurant does not offer beer or wine? _____
5 Which restaurant is not open on Sundays? _____
6 Which restaurant offers cheap drinks? _____
7 Which restaurant is expensive? _____
8 Which restaurants open every day? _____ and _____

3 Which restaurant is best for these people?

1 'I want a cheap 3-course lunch in the city centre.' _2_
2 'My boyfriend doesn't eat meat.' _____
3 'I need food for six children and one adult.' _____
4 'I want an early lunch, around eleven o'clock.' _____
5 'My wife prefers French food.' _____
6 'We're university students, and we'd like a cheap dinner before the film.' _____
7 'My girlfriend loves live music.' _____
8 'I've got only half an hour to eat before my bus leaves.' _____

4 Underline three or four words you don't know. Guess their meaning, and then check in your dictionary.

1

EL PASO
MEXICAN RESTAURANT

Try our famous chilli con carne!
DRINKS HALF-PRICE ON WEDS

Open 7 days a week,
12 p.m.–12 a.m.

Special prices for students

19 Kings Road (near cinema)
Tel. 347 5961

3

Portofino
Italian restaurant
Pasta, pizza, Italian wine

Special children's meals
Weds 6–7.30 all food half-price
Closed Tuesdays

44 Pebble St (next to bus station)
Tel. 837 4491

5

Oliver's café bar
47 Grant St   Tel. 394 7182

10 a.m.–2 a.m. Mon–Sat
Closed Sundays

2-course lunches €30

**Cocktails, wine, beers,
hot meals, tea, coffee**

LIVE MUSIC Tues/Wed/Thurs night
A warm welcome for everyone!

2

HOUSE OF LI
Chinese restaurant

Delicious Chinese food
3-course menu of the day €12

Open every day.
12 p.m.–2 a.m.

107 Queensway – 664 8329
(next to Central train station)

4

L'ESCARGOT
Fine French food and wine

◇◇◇◇◇◇◇◇◇◇◇◇◇

3-course dinner only €99

◇◇◇◇◇◇◇◇◇◇◇◇◇

Open Tues–Sun 6 p.m.–12 a.m.

*Please phone
to reserve your table*

14A Grant Street – 346 7195

6

Flowers
Vegetarian food

No meat, fish or eggs
No alcoholic drinks
Fresh vegetables from our own garden

**Lunches: 12–2.30
Evening meals: 6 p.m.–10.30 p.m.
Closed Wednesdays**

37 PARKSIDE – TEL. 329 4485

B Listen for general meaning

5 **6S.1▶** Listen to four conversations. Number the pictures.

a ☐

b ☐

c ☐

d ☐

6 Put the first conversation in order.

A ☐ Thank you, madam.
A ☐ Would you like any wine?
A ☑ Is the food all right, madam?
A ☐ Would you like a bottle or glass?
A ☐ Red or white?

B ☐ Yes, thank you. It's fine.
B ☐ Ah, yes, please.
B ☐ Oh, er, a bottle please. A bottle of red wine.
B ☐ Red, please.

7 Check the audio script on » p.92.

C Write about your favourite food

8 Complete the text with these words.
much   any   usually   ~~food~~   some

My favourite ¹ _food_____
is Chinese fried rice.
It's got rice, and there's
² _____ some
meat in it, ³ _____
egg, different vegetables
and salt. But there isn't
⁴ _____ butter in it.
The Chinese don't use butter
very ⁵ _____.

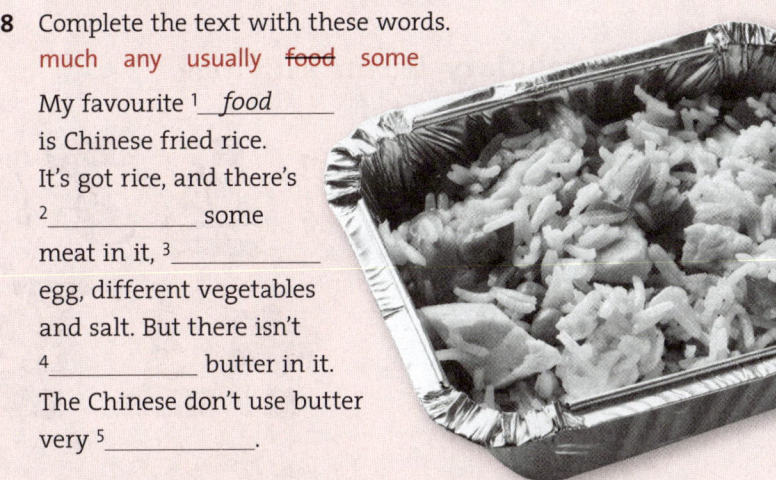

9 Read about Jim's favourite food. Correct eight more
spelling mistakes.

    favourite
My ~~favrite~~ food is Italian. It's called risotto and

my ant makes a delicious one. It's got rice and beens

and meet, and lots of vegetables – onyons, carots,

peaz and tomatoes. Oh, and some chease too.

And we usually have a botle of red wine with it.

10 Write five sentences about your favourite food.
*My favourite food is ...*_____
_____
_____
_____
_____

11 Check your writing for spelling mistakes.

Now try the Self check on » p.81.

How to **talk about free-time activities**

v leisure activities

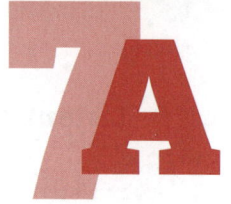

A **Vocabulary** leisure activities

1 Write the words.

1 _f i s h i n g_
2 s _ _ _ _ _ _
3 g _ _ _ _ _
4 b _ _ _ _ _ _ _ _ _
5 c _ _ _ _
6 r _ _ _ _ _-_ _ _ _ _
7 a r _ _
8 the g _ _
9 a s _ _ _
10 the p _ _ _
11 a w _ _ _
12 t _ _ _ _ t _ _ _ _ _

2 Write the words from exercise 1 in the correct box.

go	go **for**	go **to**	play	play **the**
fishing	_____	_____	_____	_____
_____	_____	_____	_____	_____
_____	_____	_____	_____	_____

3 Add any more words you know.

4 Read the text and put the pictures in order.

A relaxing weekend in the city

Well, I don't have a lot of free time. One of the first things I do at the weekend is buy a newspaper, find a café somewhere, and sit and read all the news. That relaxes me a lot. I always go for a walk, too – I need some fresh air after a week in the office, you know! And then sometimes, if I feel really active, I get my bicycle out and ride, maybe round the park, maybe in the countryside. Anything to change the routine, really. In the afternoon, I go and watch the football. After the match, I go out with my friends for a drink, usually to one of the pubs in town. And then at night we go to a disco. I love dancing. I love the music. Then on Sunday I've got another 24 hours to relax more!

5 Complete the conversation with these words.

~~often~~ go swim not
what there ever buy

A How [1] _often_ do you have holidays?

B Usually twice a year – in August and December.

A [2] _____ do you usually do?

B Well, I sometimes [3] _____ to the beach, you know.

A What do you do [4] _____?

B I often go fishing. I go for a [5] _____ every day, and I go to a restaurant about twice a week.

A Do you [6] _____ go sailing?

B No, [7] _____ really. It's very expensive.

A Do you [8] _____ gifts for your family?

B Oh, yes! Always!

And you? Answer the questions in exercise 5.

1
2
3
4
5

How well can you talk about free-time activities now?
Go back to the Student's Book >> p.67 and tick ✓ the line again.

How to **talk about the weather**

G *Let's ..., How about ...*   **V** weather   **P** /w/

 A **Vocabulary** weather

1 Look at the weather table and answer the questions.

Beijing		10°	Moscow		−10°
Buenos Aires		26°	New Delhi		23°
Cairo		44°	Tehran		−5°
Jakarta		38°	Tokyo		13°
Lima		24°	Warsaw		2°

What's the weather like in ...

1 Tokyo? *It's rainy and cool* .
2 Cairo? _____ .
3 Lima? _____ .
4 Tehran? _____ .
5 Beijing? _____ .
6 Jakarta? _____ .
7 Warsaw? _____ .
8 Buenos Aires? _____ .
9 New Delhi? _____ .
10 Moscow? _____ .

B **Grammar** *Let's ..., How about ...*

2 Underline the correct words.
1 Let's have / having some coffee!
2 How about watch / watching TV?
3 Let's go / going for a walk!
4 How about some music / play some music?
5 Let's go fishing / fish.
6 How about go / going for a drink?
7 Let's going / go to the park!
8 How about a DVD / get a DVD?
9 Let's playing / play basketball!
10 How about reading / read in the garden?

3 Write a suggestion for each picture. Use *Let's ...* or *How about ...?*

1 *How about going to the shops?*
2 _____
3 _____
4 _____
5 _____
6 _____
7 _____
8 _____

4 Put the conversation in order.
A ☐ How about a game of tennis?
A ☐ Well, roller-skating is warm! Let's go roller-skating.
A ☐ 1 It's ten o'clock. What shall we do today?
A ☐ OK – **you** make a suggestion!

B ☐ I don't know. What would you like to do?
B ☐ Let's just stay in!
B ☐ Oh, it's cloudy and cold!
B ☐ I haven't got any roller-skates.

C **Pronunciation** /w/

5 Underline the words with the sound /w/.
weather what answer question windy when
snow week swim view where how why write

6 Check your answers in your dictionary. Practise saying the words.

How well can you talk about the weather and make suggestions now?
Go back to the Student's Book >> p.69 and tick ✓ the line again.

41

How to **describe abilities**

G *can, can't*; adverbs   V abilities   P unstressed *can*, stressed *can't*

A **Vocabulary** abilities

1 Match the verbs and the nouns.
1 [g] play
2 [ ] climb
3 [ ] cook
4 [ ] draw
5 [ ] play
6 [ ] drive
7 [ ] speak
8 [ ] understand

a a car, a bus, a train, a lorry
b a picture, a person, an object, an animal
c another language
d eggs, fish, meat, rice, dinner
e a wall, a tree, a mountain
f a short conversation, a long text
g ~~football, tennis, basketball~~
h the piano, the guitar

B **Grammar** *can, can't*; adverbs

2 Complete the conversation with *can* or *can't*.

Satomi Ana! I need your help!

Ana What's wrong?

S I ¹ *can't* do my homework!

A Why not?

S I ² _____ understand this part.

A Yes, you ³ _____!

S No, I ⁴ _____! It's very difficult! ⁵ _____ you do it?

A Oh, I ⁶ _____ do it, but it's not my homework!

S Oh, please! It's late and I want to go out.

A All right, all right – let's read it together.

3 Complete the sentences with the adverbs.
1 He can speak Arabic very *slowly* . slow
2 She can climb a tree _____ . easy
3 I can skate, but not very _____ . good
4 He can drive, but _____ . bad
5 They can swim, but not very _____ . quick

4 Write sentences about Bob and Lucy.

WORK IN CHINA!
- Can you drive?
- Can you use a computer?
- Do you want to learn Chinese?

Come and work with us!

KEY		Bob	Lucy
✓✓✓ = well			
✓✓ = yes, I can			
✓ = yes, but not very well			
✗ = no, I can't			
drive		✓	✓✓✓
use a computer		✓✓	✓✓✓
write business letters		✓✓✓	✓✓
read Chinese		✓	✗
speak Chinese		✗	✓

1 *Bob can drive, but not very well* _____ .
2 _____ .
3 _____ .
4 _____ .
5 _____ .
6 _____ .

C **Pronunciation** *can, can't*

5 Complete the sentences with these words.
fast Spanish anything name ~~bus~~ football

She can drive a ¹ *bus* _____ ,
she can run ² _____ ,
and she can understand ³ _____ ,
but she **can't** cook ⁴ _____ ,
she **can't** play ⁵ _____ ,
and she **can't** remember my ⁶ _____ !

6 **7C.1▶** Listen and repeat. Copy the pronunciation of *can* and *can't*.

And you? Write five sentences about things that you can and can't do.
1
2
3
4
5

How well can you describe abilities now?
Go back to the Student's Book >> p.71 and tick ✓ the line again.

How to **talk about likes and dislikes**

G *like doing; like sth* **V** likes and dislikes **P** *hate* /h/

A Vocabulary **likes and dislikes**

1 Fill the gaps with these verbs.

going watching listening to taking ~~meeting~~
reading talking playing doing

1 *meeting* friends, people
2 _____ homework, housework, exercise
3 _____ cards, video games, sports
4 _____ radio, music, CDs
5 _____ dancing, fishing, swimming
6 _____ to friends, on the phone, on the Internet
7 _____ TV, DVDs, football
8 _____ photos, the dog for a walk
9 _____ books, newspapers, magazines

2 Add other words you know, or look in your dictionary.

B Grammar *like doing; like sth*

3 Write the words in the correct place in the sentences.

    dogs   *taking*
1 I like but I don't like them for a walk!
   dogs, taking

2 I like on TV and I love them at the cinema.
   films, watching

3 I love to the beach but I don't like.
   going, the mountains

4 I like books but I don't enjoy.
   reading, magazines

5 I love to friends but I don't like the Internet.
   talking, using

6 I enjoy a good but I don't like!
   meal, cooking

7 I like sports but I don't like them!
   watching, playing

8 I love tea but I don't like it.
   drinking, making

9 I enjoy but I hate dog!
   eating, biscuits

4 Order the words to make questions.

A do cooking like you
  ¹ *Do you like cooking*   ?
B Not very much!
A cook you meals what can
  ²   ?
B Ham and eggs, sausages, toasted sandwiches – the usual.
A do you at doing what like weekends
  ³   ?
B Watching TV and meeting friends.
A exercise do any do you
  ⁴   ?
B Not really. Sometimes I go for a swim.
A the you do holidays enjoy what doing in
  ⁵   ?
B Sitting on the beach with a long drink!
A things dislike you do what
  ⁶   ?
B I don't like housework or homework. And I don't like listening to my daughter's music!

C Pronunciation *hate* /h/

5 **7D.1▶** Listen and <u>underline</u> where you hear the sound /h/.

1 <u>H</u>ello <u>H</u>enry!
2 house and home
3 half an hour
4 Who works hard?
5 She hates the housework!
6 When's your holiday?
7 I need help with my homework!

6 Listen again and repeat.

And you? Answer the questions in exercise 4.
1
2
3
4
5
6

A Listen for key information

1 **7S.1▶** Listen and number the places.

- ☐ bars
- ☐ disco
- ☑ hotel
- ☐ river
- ☐ car park
- ☐ gym
- ☐ park
- ☐ shops
- ☐ cinema
- ☐ hairdresser's
- ☐ restaurants
- ☐ swimming pool

2 Listen again and put the questions in order.

- ☐ All right?
- ☐ Any questions?
- ☐ OK?
- ☐ Can you see that?
- ☑ Have you got that?

3 Check the audio script on ≫ p.93.

B Read and understand a brochure

4 Read the brochure and write these headings in the correct place.

Pets   Adults   Young Children   Teenagers

5 Write *true* or *false*.

1 There aren't any dance classes for young children.   *True*

2 Adults use the gym in the afternoons.   _____

3 Young children have cinema films three days a week.   _____

4 They offer study classes for adults.   _____

5 Boating is for adults.   _____

6 There are water sports for teenagers on Fridays.   _____

7 Adults have dance classes in the disco.   _____

8 Teenagers can go to the disco four nights a week.   _____

9 Young children play sports in the afternoons.   _____

10 Dogs and cats have training classes together.   _____

Holiday Out Club

1

- Water games in the children's pool, 3.00 to 6.00 every afternoon (In bad weather, these activities are in the gym)
- Sports activities in the gym, every morning from 9.00 to 10.30
- TV room with children's channels
- Reading room with comics, picture books and magazines
- Park for small children
- Lunchtime cinema, Mon Wed Fri 1.00

2

- Dance classes in the disco, mornings from 9.30 to 12.00
- Summer study classes, mornings from 9.00 to 11.00
- Water sports in the swimming pool 2.00 to 5.00 every day. Competitions at weekends (2 groups: 13–15 year-olds; 16–17 year-olds)
- Disco from 8.00 to 12.00, Thurs Fri Sat Sun
- Cinema with 5 different films every week
- Reading room with books and magazines
- Internet room

3

- Reading room with international newspapers and magazines
- Dance classes and exercises in the gym, every morning from 10.30 to 12.30 (2 groups: 18–30 year-olds; over 30s)
- Cinema with 5 different films every week
- TV and Internet room
- Boating on the river
- Fishing in the river
- Excursions

4

- Special area in the park
- Dog-walking service
- Vet available
- Training classes for you and your dog (Sat) or cat (Sun)

C Read an interview

6 Read the interview with a dancer.

Interviewer Now, Lizzie, could I just ask you ...

Lizzie Hi! My name's Lizzie Bop! I'm the star of my dance group. I want to say I just love your magazine. It's the best magazine in the shops! I really enjoy talking about myself and my life, you know?

I Thank you. Can you tell our readers about your work?

L I work very hard but I really love it. We only perform two or three nights a week, but we rehearse almost every day, sometimes for twelve hours a day. Maybe that's why I love my days off too! I like getting up late in the morning, at about eleven o'clock. I enjoy reading the newspaper and having my breakfast in bed. You see, most days I don't have time for those things.

I I see. And what else do you do when you're not working?

L I'll tell you what I don't do: I don't do the housework. I hate it! I don't really like shopping either – except for clothes, of course! – or cooking or washing the dishes. Sometimes I visit my friends and family at the weekend, but I like staying at home too. Maybe you think I'm a bit dull! I also like spending time with my dogs. I just love those dogs – they're my best friends. They can be a problem though – I have my meals in restaurants, and often they're not allowed to go in with me.

7 Tick ✓ the things Lizzie likes.
1 ✓ talking about herself
2 ☐ her work
3 ☐ breakfast in bed
4 ☐ visiting friends
5 ☐ cooking
6 ☐ getting up late
7 ☐ washing dishes
8 ☐ her dogs

8 Match the words with their meanings. Then check in your dictionary.
1 c̲ star
2 ☐ perform
3 ☐ rehearse
4 ☐ housework
5 ☐ dull
6 ☐ not allowed

  a boring
  b told you can't do something
  c ~~a famous person~~
  d do something again and again to get better
  e work you do at home (cooking, cleaning ...)
  f do a play, concert, etc. in front of people

D Write about a day off

9 Complete the text with these phrases.

on their last day off ~~two months~~ or play sports
half an hour work on Sundays

João is from Portugal. Every summer he spends [1] _two months_ picking grapes on a farm in France. The days are long, from six in the morning to six in the evening, but the workers have two hours for lunch. They also have [2] _____ for breakfast at eight o'clock in the morning, and they don't [3] _____. Sunday is their day off, and they usually play music or go for a walk. They don't watch TV [4] _____. [5] _____, João and the others have a party and say goodbye until next year.

10 What do you do when you have a day off? Write four or five sentences.

_____
_____
_____
_____
_____

11 Check your writing for mistakes.

Now try the Self check on ›› p.82.

How to **invite and reply**

G *I'd like ..., Would you like ...?* **V** social phrases **P** *for* and *to*

A Vocabulary social phrases

1 Complete the sentences with these phrases.

for a drink   ~~for a walk~~   to the shops
to the park   to the gym   for a coffee
to the cinema   to the pool   for a run

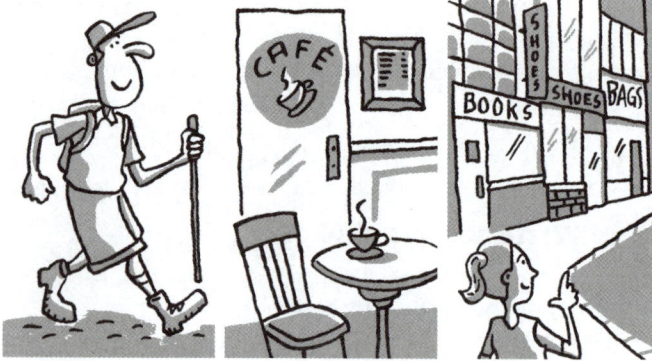

1 I'm going
   for a walk   .

2 I'm going
   _____ .

3 She's going
   _____ .

4 She's going
   _____ .

5 I'm going
   _____ .

6 We're going
   _____ .

7 We're going
   _____ .

8 He's going
   _____ .

9 I'm going
   _____ .

2 Put the conversation in order.

A ☐1☐ Hi, Jerry. Are you busy?
A ☐ It's 11.30.
A ☐ OK, no problem.
A ☐ Yeah, I need some things.
A ☐ I'm going to the shops. Would you like to come?
B ☐ What time is it?
B ☐ Oh dear! Sorry, but I haven't got time. I need to start cooking lunch!
B ☐ No, not really. Why?
B ☐ The shops?

B Grammar *I'd like ..., Would you like ...?*

3 Underline the correct words.
1 Would you like dance / to dance?
2 I'd like a drink / drinking.
3 They'd like to go to Paris / go for Paris for the weekend.
4 Would you like a coffee? / have coffee?
5 Would you like go out / to go out for a meal?
6 We'd like an apple / having an apple.
7 She'd like be / to be alone.
8 I'd like go a walk / a walk.
9 Would you like going / to go to the park?

C Pronunciation *for* and *to*

4 Complete the sentences with *for, to, four,* or *two.*
1 **A** We usually have a snack at about *four* o'clock.
   B It's ten _____ four now. Let's eat!
2 **A** We're going _____ the football match.
   B Oh! I'd love _____ go _____ the match!
3 **A** We're going _____ a sandwich. Would you like one?
   B I'd like _____ please! One ham, one cheese.
4 **A** We're going _____ a drink! Would you like _____ come?
   B I'd love _____ come, but I've got _____ exams tomorrow – English and maths.

5 **8A.1▶** Listen and read the audio script on >> p.93.
6 Listen again and notice the different pronunciation of *for / four* and *to / two.*

How well can you invite and reply now?
Go back to the Student's Book >> p.77 and tick ✓ the line again.

How to **say what to wear**

G imperatives   V family; clothes   P *shirt* /ɜː/ or *short* /ɔː/

A **Vocabulary** family; clothes

1 Complete the sentences.

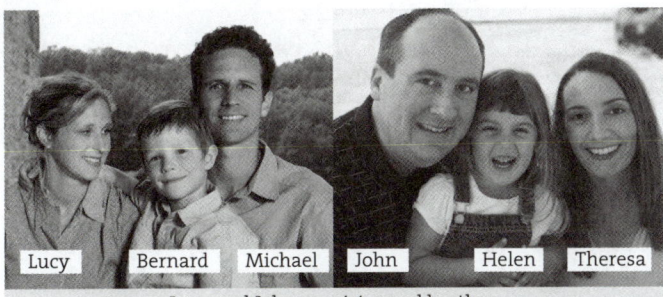

Lucy   Bernard   Michael   John   Helen   Theresa

Lucy and John are sister and brother.

1 *Michael*_____ is Bernard's father.
2 _____ is Helen's uncle.
3 _____ is Bernard's aunt.
4 _____ is John's brother-in-law.
5 _____ is Theresa's nephew.
6 _____ is Michael's niece.

2 Write the words.

1 *jeans*_____ and a T-_____
2 a sh_____ and t_____
3 a h_____ and c_____
4 a j_____ and tr_____
5 sh_____ and s_____
6 b_____ and sh_____
7 a s_____ and a dr_____
8 a sh_____ sk_____ and
   a l_____ sk_____
9 a sw_____ and a c_____

B **Grammar** imperatives

3 Match the instructions with the signs.
Use your dictionary.

1 [c] Cross the street!
2 [ ] Don't cross the street!
3 [ ] Don't swim here!
4 [ ] Drive this way!
5 [ ] Don't drive this way!
6 [ ] Leave your pets outside!
7 [ ] Don't use your mobile phone!
8 [ ] Don't smoke in here!
9 [ ] Don't make fires here!
10 [ ] Be careful!

C **Pronunciation** *shirt* /ɜː/ or *short* /ɔː/

4 **8B.1▶** Listen and underline the correct words.
1 I can't find my <u>shirts</u> / shorts!
2 We're going to work / walk this afternoon.
3 What's that bird / board on the tree?
4 She lives on the third / fourth floor.
5 Mum! Where are my football shorts / shirts?
6 What time do you start working / walking?
7 Smith! Is this your board / bird?
8 What's the third / fourth country on the map?

5 Listen again and repeat.

> **And you?** Answer the questions.
>
> 1 What are you wearing today?
>   _____
> 2 What are your favourite clothes for winter?
>   _____
> 3 And for summer?
>   _____

How well can you say what to wear now?
Go back to the Student's Book >> p.79 and tick ✓ the line again.

How to **say what's happening**

G present continuous ⊞ ⊟ ? **V** action verbs **P** -*ing* /ɪŋ/

A Vocabulary **action verbs**

1 Write the -*ing* form of the verbs.

1 sit _sitting_	4 look at _____	7 smile _____
2 drink _____	5 play _____	8 use _____
3 laugh _____	6 dance _____	9 write _____

B Grammar **present continuous ⊞ ⊟ ?**

2 Complete the sentences with the present continuous. Use the verbs in exercise 1.

1 He _'s_ _sitting_ on a desk.
2 She ____ _____ to the music.
3 He ____ _____ .
4 ____ she _____ in a notebook?
5 ____ he _____ the phone?
6 She ____ _____ computer games.
7 He ____ _____ .
8 They ____ _____ photos.
9 He ____ _____ coffee.

3 Complete the conversation.

A What ¹_are you doing_____ (you / do), darling?
B Sh! ²_____ (I / listen to) the neighbours!
A What ³_____ (they / do)?
B Mrs Jones ⁴_____ (talk) to someone.
A What ⁵_____ (she / say)?
B ⁶_____ (she / talk) to Mr Jones.
   Oh, ⁷_____ (they / talk) about us!

C Pronunciation -*ing* /ɪŋ/

4 Complete the phrases with these words.

bath bike car exercises dinner
~~nothing~~ park speaking you

1 something – anything – _nothing_
2 reading – writing – _____
3 driving a _____
4 walking in the _____
5 riding a _____
6 making _____
7 doing _____
8 having a _____
9 thinking about _____

5 **8C.1▶** Listen and check.
Repeat all the phrases.

And you? Answer the questions.
Use your dictionary if necessary.

1 When do you go dancing?
   I often go dancing at the weekend.

2 Do you usually write letters
   or emails? _____

   _____

3 What do you drink when you
   go out? _____

   _____

4 What sports do you play?

   _____

   _____

5 Where in the classroom do you
   usually sit? _____

   _____

6 What makes you laugh?

   _____

   _____

How well can you say what's happening now?
Go back to the Student's Book >> p.81 and tick ✓ the line again.

How to describe actions

G present simple and present continuous   P contrastive stress

A Grammar present simple and present continuous

1   Underline the correct words.

1 Usually, Tench gets up / is getting up at 8.00,
   but today she's having / she has breakfast at 8.00.
2 Today is different. Today she doesn't go / isn't going
   to work.
3 She always is taking / takes a notebook,
   but today she's taking / she takes a map, too.
4 She usually arrives / is arriving at work at 9.00,
   but today she's going / she goes to the airport.
5 It's 11.00 and she waits / is waiting for someone.
   Usually she is having / has a coffee break at 11.00.
6 Most days she looks / is looking at a computer screen.
   Today she looks at / is looking at a man's face.
7 She normally is going / goes home after work,
   but today she flies / is flying to another country.
8 She is having / has an interesting day today!

2   Complete the text with the verbs in brackets in the present simple or present continuous.

Onderkofer is a special agent. His life is interesting – he ¹ _meets_ (meet) a lot of people, he ² _____ (travel) to different places, and he ³ _____ (eat) different food. The only problem is that his work is a secret. He can never tell people what he is really doing when he meets them.

Anyway, today he's in Prague, in the Czech Republic. Today he's a tourist: he ⁴ _____ (wear) jeans and boots, a pink shirt and glasses. He ⁵ _____ (carry) a camera and a guide book. He's got a meeting at eleven o'clock. At 10.45, he is in a café near the church. There are three people inside. One man is at the window. He ⁶ _____ (drink) coffee. A woman near the door ⁷ _____ (write) in a notebook. Another man ⁸ _____ (watch) the TV on the wall. He ⁹ _____ (wear) jeans and boots, a pink shirt and glasses, and has a camera and guide book too. Onderkofer looks and looks at the man. 'What ¹⁰ _____ (you do) here?' he asks him.

B Pronunciation contrastive stress

3   Complete the sentences with these words.

he she ~~they~~ him her us
~~us~~ her him they she he

1 **We**'re watching **them**, but _they_
   aren't watching _us_ .
2 **He**'s looking at **her**, but _____
   isn't looking at _____ .
3 **She** likes **him**, but _____
   doesn't like _____ .
4 **He** always phones **her**, but _____
   never phones _____ !
5 **We** sometimes invite **them**, but
   _____ don't invite _____ !
6 **She** talks about **him**, but _____
   doesn't talk about _____ .

4   **8D.1▶** Listen and check.
Copy the stress.

And you? Complete the sentences.

1 Usually I wear _____ ,
   but today I'm wearing _____
   _____ .

2 Usually I do my homework
   _____ , but today
   I'm doing it _____ .

3 Usually I _____ ,
   but today _____ .

Unit 8 Skills Practice

A Read for detail

1 Read the text. Are the tips for men (M), women (W) or men and women (MW)?

Dress for Success

Is it important how you dress at an interview? Is it OK to wear jeans and a T-shirt? Jenny Tinker is an interviewer for a big London company. She thinks it is very important! 'Some people come to an interview in the wrong clothes,' she says. 'I never give a job to a man in shorts and sandals, a woman in a miniskirt, or anyone in jeans.' Here are ten tips to help you in your next interview.

1 Wear a suit and tie for an interview for an office job.
   _M_

2 Wear dark shoes and clean them before the interview.
   _MW_

3 Take off your hat before you sit down.
   _____

4 Wear a jacket and a long skirt or trousers.
   _____

5 Don't wear a lot of jewellery.
   _____

6 Don't wear jeans. You are going to an interview, not to the pub!
   _____

7 Don't wear a very short skirt.
   _____

8 Have a normal hairstyle, and it's good if it's not green!
   _____

9 Don't wear a lot of aftershave.
   _____

10 For an interview for a factory job, wear comfortable, clean clothes – but not jeans!
   _____

2 Write *true* or *false*.
1 It's good to wear black jeans, but not blue ones. _False_
2 Jenny Tinker thinks how you dress at interviews is important. _____
3 It is OK to clean your shoes in the interview. _____
4 A long skirt is good, but not a short skirt. _____
5 Green hair is good for interviews. _____
6 Leave your hat at home. _____
7 Yellow shoes are good, but not black ones. _____

3 <u>Underline</u> three or four words you don't know. Guess their meaning, and then check in your dictionary.

B Listen for detail

4 8S.1▶ A spy is watching a man in the station. Listen and tick ✓ the man he is describing.

5 Listen again. Complete these phrases with the adjectives you hear.

1 a _tall_ man
2 _____ _____ hair
3 a _____ _____ coat
4 a _____ tie
5 _____ shoes

6 Check the audio script on » p.93.

C Read film reviews

7 Match the texts and the pictures.

a b c

1 Rear Window
Alfred Hitchcock, 1954

Starring James Stewart **RATING *****

THE STORY: A man lives in his apartment in a wheelchair. He can't walk, run or stand. He spends all his time sitting in his wheelchair, looking out of the window. He can see many of the neighbours in their apartments. He can see them cooking, eating, playing with their children – and arguing. One day, he sees a man argue with his wife, and then he can't see the wife. He thinks the man kills his wife ...

THE ACTORS: In my opinion, Stewart is excellent ...

2 Black Rain
Ridley Scott, 1989

Starring Michael Douglas **RATING ****

THE STORY: An American policeman travels to Japan with a Japanese criminal. But the criminal escapes in the airport, and the policeman helps the Japanese police to find him again ...

THE ACTORS: Douglas is another American policeman with a big motorbike ...

3 Amélie
Jean-Pierre Jeunet, 2001

Starring Audrey Tautou **RATING *****

THE STORY: Amélie lives alone and works in a café. She sees the same customers every day and she often thinks about a different life – a life with love. She spends a lot of time making other people happy. But then she meets a man ...

THE ACTORS: Audrey Tautou is superb as Amélie ...

8 Match the words with the meanings. Then check in your dictionary.

1 [c] wheelchair
2 [ ] argue
3 [ ] criminal
4 [ ] escape
5 [ ] superb

a talk in an angry way with someone
b get away from somebody, e.g. a policeman
c ~~a chair with wheels for someone who can't walk~~
d very good
e a person who does something against the law

D Write a review

9 Complete the text with these words.
love got has puts boring ~~is~~

Film title: Diva

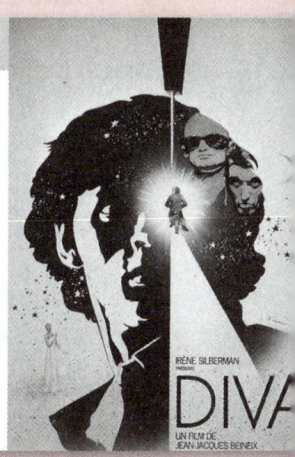

Year: 1981
Director: Jean-Jacques Beineix

■ **THE STORY:** Jules ¹ _is_ a postman. He is in ² _____ with Cynthia, who is an opera singer (she is the Diva). He ³ _____ a lot of problems when somebody ⁴ _____ a video tape in his postbag.

■ **THE FILM:** This is a marvellous film. It's ⁵ _____ love and action. The film is fresh, and never ⁶ _____. I really love the photography.

10 Read the text. <u>Underline</u> three more adjectives.

Film title: Snakes On A Plane

Year: 2006
Director: David R. Ellis

■ **THE STORY:** Hundreds of <u>dangerous</u> snakes are on a plane, and so is an FBI agent, Neville Flynn (Samuel L. Jackson). He is taking an important witness to Los Angeles. Only Flynn can save the plane and kill the snakes before they kill all the terrified passengers.

■ **THE FILM:** This is a silly film – you can enjoy the action and have a good laugh.

11 Think of a film you know well. Write a short review.

Film title: _____

Year: _____ Director: _____

Write three sentences about the story:
_____
_____
_____

Write three sentences about why you liked or didn't like the film:
_____
_____
_____

12 Check your sentences for mistakes. Can you add one or two adjectives?

Now try the Self check on >> p.83.

How to **ask for transport information**

A Vocabulary **instruction phrases**

1 Match the places and the instructions. Start at the Gare du Nord.

1 [c] Take the B or D train line south to Châtelet Les Halles. Change to the metro, Line 1. Get off at the fifth stop west.

2 ☐ Take the metro, Line 4, south. It's 13 stops after that. You don't need to change trains.

3 ☐ Take the B train line south. It's one stop after St Michel Notre Dame.

4 ☐ Take the B train line south to St Michel Notre Dame. Change to another train, the C line, and travel west. It's the fourth stop.

5 ☐ Take the metro, Line 4, north. Get off at the next stop. Change to Line 2, and go west. Get off at the next stop, and walk from there.

6 ☐ Take the metro, Line 4, south. Get off at Réaumur Sébastopol. Change to Line 3, and go west. It's the fourth stop.

  a Opéra   d Tour Eiffel
  b Montmartre   e Montparnasse
  c ~~Champs Elysées~~   f La Sorbonne

B Vocabulary **transport**

2 Write the transport words.

1 *departure gate*

6 _____

2 _____

7 _____

3 _____

8 _____

4 _____

9 _____

5 _____

C Pronunciation **polite intonation**

3 **9A.1▶** Listen. Do the speakers sound polite (P) or rude (R)?

1 [R] Excuse me, how can I get to the museum, please?
2 [P] Excuse me, how can I get to the museum, please?

3 ☐ Excuse me, how can I get to the airport, please?
4 ☐ Excuse me, how can I get to the airport, please?

5 ☐ Excuse me, how can I get to the hospital, please?
6 ☐ Excuse me, how can I get to the hospital, please?

7 ☐ Excuse me, how can I get to the park, please?
8 ☐ Excuse me, how can I get to the park, please?

4 Listen again. Copy the polite intonation.

How well can you ask for transport information now?
Go back to the Student's Book >> p.87 and tick ✓ the line again.

How to give and follow directions

v places in town; directions   **P** linking words together

A Vocabulary places in town

1 Complete the crossword.

Across

3 9 5 10 7 11

Down

1 6 2 8 4 9

Across 3: p o l i c e s t a t i o n

B Vocabulary directions

2 Complete the directions.

1 from the bank in Argyle Street to the health centre:
Go along Argyle Street _to_ Mitchell Street.
Turn _left_, and go _____ on. It's at the _____
corner _____ the left.

2 from Glasgow Bridge to St Enoch shopping centre:
Go along Jamaica Street and turn _____ into
Howard Street. Go straight _____ and it's on
the _____.

3 from St Enoch underground station to the post office:
Go _____ of the station into Argyle Street, and
_____ left. The post office is _____ the
corner _____ the bank.

C Pronunciation linking words together

3 **9B.1▶** Listen. Where one word ends with a consonant
sound and the next word begins with a vowel sound,
write ‿.

1 It's the first left‿at the corner.

2 There's a bank at the corner.

3 The post office is just opposite.

4 Go straight on and turn left at the lights.

5 The map says there's an art gallery near here.

6 It's across the bridge and on the left.

7 Turn right again into Union Street.

8 I think there's a tourist information office in the station.

4 Listen again and repeat. Do you link words like this in
your language?

How to **ask about and describe a holiday**

G past simple of *be* ⊞⊟? *was, were, wasn't, weren't*   V adjectives; holidays   P *is, was, are, were*

A **Vocabulary** adjectives; holidays

1 ~~Cross out~~ the wrong adjective.

1 The weather is   lovely   warm   ~~noisy~~   horrible
2 The people are   boring   unfriendly   crowded   polite
3 The beach is   crowded   quiet   polite   empty
4 The hotel is   clean   comfortable   wet   expensive
5 The room is   small   dirty   uncomfortable   friendly
6 The food is   uncomfortable   cheap   delicious   awful
7 The shops are   expensive   full   delicious   boring
8 The nightlife is   empty   fantastic   cheap   awful

2 Write these adjectives in the correct box.

~~clean~~   ~~dirty~~   lovely   beautiful   comfortable   horrible
boring   unfriendly   polite   exciting   uncomfortable
awful   delicious   interesting   fantastic

positive	negative
clean	*dirty*

B **Grammar** past simple of *be* ⊞⊟? *was, were, wasn't, weren't*

3 Complete the conversation with *was, were, wasn't,* or *weren't*.

A ¹ *Were* you in another country?

B Yes, I ² _____.

A ³ _____ you alone?

B No, I ⁴ _____.

A ⁵ _____ your boyfriend with you?

B Yes, he ⁶ _____.

A ⁷ _____ you on a beach?

B No, we ⁸ _____.

A ⁹ _____ you in the mountains?

B Yes, we ¹⁰ _____.

A What ¹¹ _____ the weather like?

B It ¹² _____ very cold!

A ¹³ _____ you walking in the mountains?

B No, we ¹⁴ _____.

A ¹⁵ _____ you skiing?

B Yes, that's right! We ¹⁶ _____ skiing!

C **Pronunciation** *is, was, are, were*

4 Complete the phrases with *is* or *are*.

The beach __*is*__ nice
The boys _____ fun
The water _____ warm
In the holiday sun
But my parents _____ here
But my parents _____ here

5 Complete the phrases with *was* or *were*.

The food __*was*__ good
The weather _____ great
The drinks _____ cheap
The bars opened late
But our daughter _____ there
But our daughter _____ there

6 **9C.1▶** Listen and check.

7 Listen again and repeat. Notice the pronunciation of *is, was, are,* and *were*.

And you? Answer the questions about your last holiday.

1 Where were you?   _____

2 Were you in a hotel?   _____

3 Was there any rain?   _____

4 Were the people nice?   _____

5 What was the food like?   _____

6 Would you like to go back?   _____

7 Why / why not?   _____

How well can you ask about and describe a holiday now?
Go back to the Student's Book >> p.91 and tick ✓ the line again.

How to **tell a story**

G past simple ⊞ regular *-ed*   P *-ed* endings

A Grammar past simple ⊞ regular *-ed*

1 Write the past forms of these verbs.

1 happen   *happened*
2 look   _____
3 notice   _____
4 relax   _____
5 walk   _____
6 decide   _____
7 stay   _____
8 play   _____
9 talk   _____
10 want   _____

2 Complete the story with the verbs from exercise 1.

Holidays? Don't talk to me about holidays! We had a terrible holiday last year. Let me tell you what ¹*happened*. We ²_____ a different holiday, so we ³_____ to go camping. We ⁴_____ at a campsite near the beach. It was a beautiful place, very quiet. We ⁵_____ a lot. We went fishing and swimming, and we went sailing on some small boats. It was great!

One day after lunch, the children ⁶_____ in the water, and we ⁷_____ together outside the tent. Later we ⁸_____ to the village. We ⁹_____ at the shops, we had coffee and then it was time to go back to the tent. But the tent wasn't there! Then we ¹⁰_____ two things: nobody else had their tents near the water, and there was something red in the sea. Our tent? Oh no! That was our tent in the sea!!

3 Order the words to make the beginning of *Nightmare Hotel*.

1 up I walked hill the
   I walked up the hill
2 Hotel to Nightmare the
   _____
3 at I door the stopped
   _____
4 I see couldn't but bell the
   _____
5 knocked waited I and I
   _____
6 the windy cold in and night
   _____
7 in window looked the I
   _____
8 there but any wasn't light
   _____

B Pronunciation *-ed* endings

4 Complete the sentences with these words.

town ~~bus stop~~ umbrella
way rain help question

He waited at the
   *bus stop*_____.

It started to
   _____.

He opened his
   _____.

A voice asked him to
   _____.

He answered her
   _____.

They walked into
   _____.

They talked all the
   _____.

And who knows what happened after that!

5 **9D.1▶** Listen and check. Repeat the *-ed* verbs.

How well can you understand and tell a story now?
Go back to the Student's Book >> p.93 and tick ✓ the line again.

55

Unit 9 Skills Practice

A Read about a holiday

1 Match the pictures and the words. Use your dictionary.

a [ ]   b [ ]   c [ ]   d [*1*]   e [ ]

1 a bear   2 a coast   3 a cork   4 an island   5 a skull

2 Read the text and draw the route on the map.

My friends went to Ireland last summer to visit the beautiful west coast. They started their holiday at Cork. They stayed there for two days and visited the church and the shops. They also went by bus to Blarney Castle. Then they travelled by car to Baltimore and spent a day fishing. The next day they went to the town of Skull. There they travelled by boat and sailed round to Bear Island. The weather was good there, so they went for a long walk. Their next stop was Valentia Island on the famous Ring of Kerry. They wanted to watch animals in the sea, but it rained all day. It rains very often in this part of Ireland! After that, they stopped at Castleisland, where they had lunch. Then they went to Newcastle West to visit some friends, and finally they arrived at Limerick. There they played golf, and visited the castle and the gift shops. They enjoyed their holiday very much!

3 Match 1–8 with a–h.

1 [*d*] Baltimore   a They went for a walk.
2 [ ] Bear Island   b They visited friends.
3 [ ] Castleisland   c They played golf.
4 [ ] Cork   d ~~They spent a day fishing~~.
5 [ ] Limerick   e It rained a lot.
6 [ ] Newcastle West   f They went sailing.
7 [ ] Skull   g They went to the church.
8 [ ] Valentia Island   h They had lunch.

B Listen for general meaning

4 **9S.1▶** Listen to Sarah talking about her holiday in France. Put the events in order.

a [ ] travelled into the mountains
b [ ] arrived at the youth hostel
c [ ] watched a woman working
d [ ] talked a lot
e [*1*] travelled to Lyon

5 Write *true* or *false*.

1 Sarah's flight was expensive.   *False*
2 She got a flight to Lyon.   _____
3 She travelled east into the mountains. _____
4 She met a friend from work.   _____
5 Her friend's name was Brian.   _____
6 It rained every day.   _____

6 Listen again and complete the text.

Well, I went to France *last* _____, on a _____ _____. I stayed in youth hostels, you know, where _____ _____ _____ lots of _____ _____, and they tell you all the _____ _____ to visit.

7 Check the audio script on >> p.93.

C Read and understand a story

8 Read the story and put the paragraphs in order.

a ☐ On her first day, she and the other tourists left the hotel early in the morning on a special safari bus. They went with a guide, and he answered all their questions. Everyone had their cameras ready to take photos of the animals.

b ☐1☐ My friend Dana's a dentist. She works hard and makes a lot of money. She isn't married and she hasn't got any brothers or sisters, so she's got a lot of free time. Maybe that's why her favourite hobby is travelling.

c ☐ Everyone was worried because the elephants were very big, and the bus was very small. But then something incredible happened. One of the elephants pushed the bus out of the mud and onto the road. The tourists smiled and laughed, and Dana took some wonderful photos.

d ☐ Dana visits a different country every year, and last year she decided to go to Africa, to Kenya. She wanted to go on safari, to see the wild animals there.

e ☐ Suddenly there was a problem. The bus was stuck in the mud. It couldn't move forwards or backwards. And then three enormous elephants appeared. The tourists were very happy and took lots of photos. But then the elephants came near the bus and the tourists were all quiet.

9 Match the words with their meanings.

1	e guide	a	something you like doing when you aren't working
2	☐ hobby		
3	☐ worried	b	can't move
4	☐ stuck	c	very big
5	☐ mud	d	soft wet earth
6	☐ enormous	e	~~person who shows and tells you about a place~~
		f	unhappy about something that could happen

D Write about holidays

10 The highlighted words are spelled wrong. Can you correct them?

uncle
When I was 14, my family, my aunt and oncle, and my my cosins all visited Portugal. It was our first holiday in another contry, and it was very exciting. We stayed in a big house with a swimming pool. The people were very frenly, the weather was sunny and hot, and the food was delicous. We went for long walks on the beech, my mother and my ant did some shopping, and my father read his books. We all bought gifts to take home. It was an espensive holiday, but not for me – I didn't pay for it!

11 Are the highlighted words nouns or adjectives? Use your dictionary.

Example

uncle o̶ /ˈʌŋkl/ *noun*
the brother of your mother or father, or the husband of your aunt: *Uncle Paul*

Oxford Essential Dictionary

12 Think about a holiday when you were a child. Make notes in the table.

How old were you?	
Where did you go?	
Who did you go with?	
What were the people like?	
What was the food like?	
What was the weather like?	
What did you do?	
What did you like?	

13 Write about your holiday.
When I was ... _____

_____

_____

_____

14 Check your writing for spelling mistakes.

Now try the Self check on >> p.84.

How to **continue a conversation**

G past simple; ? *wh-* questions   P stress in *wh-* questions

A **Grammar** past simple ?

1 Match the questions and answers.

1 *f* When was the last time you went away?
2 ☐ Where did you go?
3 ☐ Where did you stay?
4 ☐ Who did you meet?
5 ☐ Did they have a good time?
6 ☐ Did you see anything interesting?
7 ☐ Did you buy anything?
8 ☐ When did you come home?

a They said the weather wasn't very good.
b Yes, we bought some gifts in the village.
c We met some friends there.
d Yes, we saw a lot of animals.
e We came back late on Sunday evening.
f ~~A month ago, in May~~.
g We stayed in a hotel.
h We went to the mountains.

2 Write questions for the missing information.

The schoolchildren went away for the day last week. They went to ¹_____. They spent all day in the town. First they visited the ²_____ and they enjoyed it a lot. Then they met ³_____, a famous TV personality. Fantastic! They asked her ⁴_____ and she told them some very interesting stories. At one o'clock they had lunch, but the children said ⁵_____. In the afternoon, they went shopping. Julia bought ⁶_____ for her parents and spent a lot of money. Finally, they went to the cinema and saw a new film. Julia said it was a bit boring! They arrived home ⁷_____, and went straight to bed.

1 Where *did the schoolchildren go* _____?
2 What _____?
3 Who _____?
4 What _____?
5 What _____?
6 What _____?
7 When _____?

3 Match the answers with the questions in exercise 2.

a *1* To Dublin.
b ☐ Gifts.
c ☐ It wasn't very good.
d ☐ Tina Green.
e ☐ The museum.
f ☐ A lot of questions.
g ☐ After ten o'clock.

B **Pronunciation** stress in *wh-* questions

4 Match the sentences with the responses.

1 *b* I met my new boss this morning!
2 ☐ They went to a Thai restaurant.
3 ☐ My brother phoned.
4 ☐ We went shopping yesterday.
5 ☐ His children were on TV!
6 ☐ My parents are here.
7 ☐ She went away last summer.
8 ☐ It's not raining now.

●   •   •   ●

a **When** did they **come?**
b **What** did you **think?**
c **What** did they **eat?**
d **Where** did she **go?**
e **What** did you **buy?**
f **What** did they **do?**
g **When** did it **stop?**
h **What** did he **say?**

5 **10A.1▶** Listen and check. Copy the stress.

And you? Answer the questions in exercise 1.
1
2
3
4
5
6
7
8

How well can you continue a conversation now?
Go back to the Student's Book >> p.97 and tick ✓ the line again.

How to **talk about a career**

G past simple regular and irregular   V careers   P *wrote* /t/ or *rode* /d/

A Grammar past simple regular and irregular

1 Write the past simple form of the verbs.

1 leave *left*
2 buy _____
3 drive _____
4 get _____
5 have _____
6 join _____

7 become _____
8 meet _____
9 see _____
10 sell _____
11 start _____
12 work _____

2 Complete the text with the past simple verbs from exercise 1.

Chuck ¹*left*____ school when he was 16. He ²_____
a job as a bus driver, but then he ³_____ an
accident. Later, he ⁴_____ as a waiter for three years.
He ⁵_____ a girl in the restaurant, and they got
married. Unfortunately, they got divorced ten months
after that, when he ⁶_____ his wife in a car with
another man. Chuck ⁷_____ the army to forget his
problems, but he ⁸_____ an army lorry into a river,
and went back to normal life. A few months later, he got
money from an aunt, ⁹_____ a restaurant and
¹⁰_____ his own business. Five years after that, he
¹¹_____ rich and ¹²_____ the business. Now
he's writing a book about his life.

B Pronunciation *wrote* /t/ or *rode* /d/

3 **10B.1▶** Listen and underline the correct word.
1 He wrote / rode home.
2 She rides / writes like an adult.
3 We send / sent her a gift for her birthday.
4 That's Batman / a bad man!
5 It's a hard / heart job!
6 They went to town / down this morning.

4 Check the audio script on >> p.93. Listen again and repeat.

C Vocabulary careers

5 Complete the phrases.

1 a l e f t school
   b got a j__ as a l____ dr____
   c dr___ a l____ for five years
   d b_____ his own l____

2 a w___ to u_____
   b became a t_____
   c w___ abroad
   d got m_____

A Grammar past simple ⊡?

1 Complete the sentences with these verbs in the past simple, first in the positive and then in the negative.

write ~~ride~~ pay get drink leave put

1 He _rode_____ his bike to school, but he _didn't_____ _ride_____ it home.

2 He _____ an MP3 player for his birthday, but he _____ a computer.

3 She _____ the workers, but she _____ them well.

4 They _____ tea and coffee, but they _____ any alcohol.

5 She _____ to her father, but she _____ to her brother.

6 He _____ poison in the food, but he _____ it in the drinks.

7 We _____ the room, but we _____ the hotel.

2 Read the conversation. Order the words to make questions.

Ana I saw a really good TV programme last night.

Satomi it about was what

¹_What was it about_____ ?

A It was about a woman who was angry with her husband.

S angry she was why

²_____ ?

A He always came home late. She didn't know where he was.

S do did what she

³_____ ?

A She called a private detective.

S her he tell did what

⁴_____ ?

A He told her the man was with another woman.

S did the what do wife

⁵_____ ?

A She killed her husband!

S poison did use she

⁶_____ ?

A No. She prepared a bath for him.

S bath die in husband her the did

⁷_____ ?

A Yes! His wife pushed an electric fan into the water.

S body do she did what the with

⁸_____ ?

A Nothing – she called the police.

S police the say she did what to

⁹_____ ?

A She said it was an accident.

S end the happened what in

¹⁰_____ ?

A I don't know! The next part is on tonight.

S Ooh! What channel?

3 Complete the policeman's questions.

1 Where / go yesterday _Where did you go yesterday_____ ?
I went to work.

2 When / finish work _____ ?
I finished at six o'clock.

3 go straight home _____ ?
No, I didn't. I went shopping first.

4 Which shops / visit _____ ?
A lot of shops. I don't remember the names.

5 Who / meet _____ ?
Nobody.

6 kill your husband _____ ?
No, of course not!

B Pronunciation *didn't*

4 **10C.1▶** Listen and repeat the poem. Notice that *didn't* is stressed.

Tommy was a **wai**ter
Who **didn't** like his **boss**
He **didn't** really **hate** her
But he **didn't** keep his **job**

How well can you talk about what happened now?
Go back to the Student's Book >> p.101 and tick ✓ the line again.

How to talk about life stories

v years; education **P** /s/ or /z/

A Vocabulary education

1 Complete the crossword.

Across

4 $e = mc^2$

6

13

7 When you are eleven or twelve, you go to s_____ school.

9 You get this qualification after you study for three or four years at university.

14 When you are four or five you go to p_____ school.

Down

1

8

12

2 Good morning / Bonjour / Buenos días

3 In some places, secondary school is called h_____ s_____.

5 For example, Oxford, Harvard, La Sorbonne.

10 You can get this qualification if you study for one or two years

11 1789 / 1917 / 1939–45

2 Complete the sentences with words from the crossword.

1 She studied l*iterature* for two years and got a di_____.

2 He did four years of c_____ at u_____ and got a d_____.

3 She studied h_____ at h_____ s_____ but she didn't like it very much.

B Vocabulary years

3 Write the years in words.

Year	You say ...
1969	*nineteen sixty-nine*
2006	
1908	
1836	
1998	
1950	
2025	

C Pronunciation /s/ or /z/

4 **10D.1▶** Listen and <u>underline</u> the words you hear.

/s/	or	/z/
1 Greenpeace	or	green peas
2 blue ice	or	blue eyes
3 Police!	or	Please!
4 Yes, Miss	or	Yes, Ms
5 a place in the theatre	or	plays in the theatre
6 this book	or	these books

5 Check the audio script on ≫ p.93. Listen again and repeat.

And you? Answer the questions.

1 Where did you go to school / college / university?

2 What did you study? _____

3 What were your favourite subjects?

4 What subjects didn't you like?

How well can you understand and talk about life stories now?
Go back to the Student's Book ≫ p.103 and tick ✓ the line again.

Unit 10 Skills Practice

A Read and understand a life story

1 Read about Edvard Munch and complete the text with these phrases.

for the next 20 years
when he was 17
at age 18
when he died in 1944
~~when he was a boy~~

Edvard Munch was born in a small town in Norway in 1863. ¹ *When he was a boy* , his family moved to the capital, Oslo. His mother died when he was five, and then he also lost one of his brothers and a sister. ²_____, he went to university to study engineering, but he had health problems. Then the next year, ³_____, he decided to change career and become a painter. He studied art for about four years before moving to Paris in 1885.

⁴_____, he lived between Paris and Berlin. This is when he painted *The Scream*, his most famous picture. When he was 45, he had more health problems, and went back to live in Norway. His life changed, and his paintings became less pessimistic. ⁵_____, the city of Oslo built a museum for his art. In 2004, thieves stole *The Scream* from the museum, but police found the painting in 2006.

2 Guess the meaning of the highlighted words. Check in your dictionary.

3 Read the text again. Write *true* or *false*.
1 Munch was born in Oslo.   *False*
2 His mother, brother and sister died.   _____
3 He studied art after he went to Paris.   _____
4 He returned to Norway when he was ill.   _____
5 He built a museum for his paintings.   _____

B Listen for detail

4 **10S.1▶** Listen and answer the questions.

1 What <u>didn't</u> she try to kill the vet with?

a ☐ a gun   b ☐ poison   c ☐ a knife

2 How many times did she try?
a ☐ two
b ☐ three
c ☐ four

3 What happened in the end?
a ☐ she escaped
b ☐ the vet died
c ☐ the police got her

5 Listen and put the questions in order.
a ☐ Why not?
b ☐ So what did she do?
c ☐1☐ And?
d ☐ She shot him?
e ☐ So did she kill him in the end?
f ☐ Didn't she stop then?

6 Read the summary. Listen again and correct four more mistakes.

cat
The ~~dog~~ was sick, so the woman took it to the doctor's clinic, but it died. She tried to kill the vet, first with poisoned apples, second with a poisoned magazine, and third with a knife.

7 Check the audio script on >> p.93.

C Read a job advert

8 Write the headings in the correct place.

   a You get   b Applications to   c You need

Leading European chemical company
requires **AREA MANAGER**
for **POLAND**

1 _____ :

- a university degree in chemistry
- good English, fluent Polish
- minimum 5 years' experience
- to be good at working in a team
- good computer skills

2 _____ :

- excellent salary
- health insurance
- company car
- expenses

3 _____ :

Oliver Pastilla

by post:	Wilcox Employment, 44 Bread St, London W6.
by fax:	0176 – 339 4285
by email:	joboffers@wilcox.net

reference number: SS 43784

---

9 Match the highlighted words in the advert with the definitions.

1 everything you learn from doing a job *experience*
2 a business organization _____
3 speaks a language very well _____
4 money for hotels and restaurants _____
5 you don't pay for doctors or hospitals _____
6 very good _____
7 a group of people who work together _____
8 abilities / things that you can do well _____
9 a person who organizes the work of other people
_____

10 Check your answers in your dictionary.

D Write biodata

11 Read about Sonia Gandhi and complete the text with *and* or *but*.

SONIA GANDHI was born in the north of Italy in 1946. In 1964, she met Rajiv Gandhi in Cambridge. Sonia ¹ *and* Rajiv were both students. The couple got married four years later, ² _____ moved to India. Sonia ³ _____ Rajiv had two children, a boy ⁴ _____ a girl. Sonia became an Indian citizen in 1983. Many people in the Gandhi family were politicians, ⁵ _____ Rajiv was different. He worked as a pilot and Sonia worked at home. In 1982, Rajiv started a career in politics. Two years later someone assassinated his mother, the Indian prime minister. The Gandhi family had a history of tragedy, ⁶ _____ Sonia's husband was also assassinated in 1991. In 1998, Sonia finally began a career in politics and today she is the leader of a large political party.

12 Match the words with their meanings. Then check in your dictionary.

1 [c] citizen   a a person who flies a plane
2 ☐ pilot   b a person at the top of a group
3 ☐ assassinate   c ~~a person with the nationality of a country~~
4 ☐ tragedy
5 ☐ leader   d kill an important or famous person
    e a very sad event

13 Think of a person who is important for you. Make notes in the table below.

Topic	your person
born	
early life	
education	
work	
now	

14 Now write five or six sentences of biodata. Remember to use *and* or *but*.

_____

_____

_____

_____

15 Check your writing carefully.

Now try the Self check on >> p.85.

How to **make suggestions**

G *too big, not big enough* **V** holiday accommodation; suggestions **P** stress in long words

A **Vocabulary** holiday accommodation

1 Find six types of holiday accommodation and write them below.

```
      H
     O T E
    L C A M P S
   I T E S E L F - C A T
  E R I N G A P A R T M
  E N T B E D A N D B R
  E A K F A S T Y O U T
  H H O S T E L T E N T
```

bed and breakfast

_____

_____

_____

_____

_____

2 Complete the sentences with the holiday accommodation in exercise 1.

1 Let's stay in a *bed and breakfast*. We can eat lunch and dinner in town.

2 I love sleeping in a _____ when we go camping.

3 We can't stay in a _____ – I'm too old.

4 The _____ has everything we need, and there's space for 200 tents.

5 I don't like staying in a _____, because I don't want to cook and clean on holiday.

6 Let's stay in a 5-star _____. We can stay in bed all day and get room service!

B **Grammar** *too* + adjective; *not* + adjective + *enough*

3 Complete the sentences with *too* or *not enough* and the adjective.

1 This room *isn't warm enough* _____. warm

2 The ring *is too expensive* _____. expensive

3 The parking space _____. big

4 My tea _____. hot

5 This place _____. dirty

6 This taxi _____. slow

7 This museum _____. interesting

8 This place _____. quiet

9 The shops _____. far

C **Pronunciation** stress in long words

4 **11A.1▶** Listen and write the number of syllables.

1 adjective	*3*	5 interview	_____
2 conversation	_____	6 sentences	_____
3 exercise	_____	7 syllables	_____
4 information	_____	8 vocabulary	_____

5 Write the words in the correct box.

●●●	●●●●	●●●●●
adjective		

6 Listen again and repeat.

How well can you make suggestions now?
Go back to the Student's Book >> p.107 and tick ✓ the line again.

How to **say what's wrong**

G *too much / many, not enough* **V** *rooms and furniture* **P** *long and short vowel sounds*

A Vocabulary rooms and furniture

1 Complete the estate agent's advert with these words.

bath chairs cooker cupboard
fridge shower sink sofa table
~~toilet~~ washbasin

FASBUCKS
· ESTATE AGENT ·

TO RENT
large flat near town centre

3 bedrooms (2 double, 1 single)

First bathroom with ¹t*oilet*____,
²b_____, washbasin,
and ³c_____

Second bathroom with toilet,
⁴sh_____ and ⁵w_____

Living room with ⁶s_____,
⁷t_____, ⁸ch_____
and TV

Kitchen with ⁹s_____,
cupboards, ¹⁰fr_____,
and ¹¹c_____

B Grammar *too much / many* + noun, *not enough* + noun

2 Ana and Satomi are having a party for 20 people. Write sentences with *too* and *enough*.

1 *There aren't enough*____ tables.
2 *There are too many*____ chairs.
3 _____ juice.
4 _____ wine.
5 _____ food.
6 _____ glasses.
7 _____ CDs.
8 _____ space for dancing.

C Pronunciation long and short vowel sounds

3 Write these words in the correct box. Use your dictionary.

~~gym~~ ~~stay~~ ~~view~~ town golf beach park tea
shop walk sink hot farm drive pub

short vowel sound	long vowel sound	
1 vowel symbol	**2 vowel symbols**	**1 vowel + :**
gym /dʒɪm/	*stay* /steɪ/	*view* /vjuː/

4 Practise saying the words.

And you? Write an estate agent's advert for your home.

_____
_____
_____

How to **compare things**

 G comparatives   **V** adjectives   **P** *-er* endings

A   **Vocabulary** adjectives

1 Find ten adjectives in the puzzle and match them with the opposites.

H	E	L	G	E	L	S	M	A	L	L
C	C	N	D	S	E	T	A	X	E	W
C	O	M	F	O	R	T	A	B	L	E
L	L	O	A	F	W	M	N	L	Z	X
F	D	D	D	T	S	S	L	L	R	P
Q	D	E	O	V	O	O	O	O	O	E
A	P	R	N	M	T	H	I	N	S	N
M	O	N	E	W	L	T	G	G	E	S
D	O	A	B	R	H	R	S	H	E	I
X	D	I	R	T	Y	X	T	E	D	V
I	S	E	A	P	T	I	G	N	E	E

1 hard   *soft*
2 warm   _____
3 short   _____
4 old-fashioned _____
5 big   _____
6 clean   _____
7 old   _____
8 fat   _____
9 cheap   _____
10 uncomfortable _____

B   **Grammar** comparatives

2 Underline the correct words.
1 His brother's fater / fatter than he is.
2 Cities on the north coast are cooler / more cool than cities in the south.
3 My bed is more comfortable / comfortabler than the hotel bed.
4 Your room is more warm / warmer than my room.
5 Tom is better / more good than Harry.
6 That table is dirtyer / dirtier than our table.
7 John's dog is more small / smaller than the neighbour's dog.
8 The new bridge is longer / more long than the old one.

3 Compare Frank's car and Ricky's car. Use these adjectives.
~~fast~~ dirty comfortable old good expensive bad

Frank

Ricky

1 *Ricky's car is faster than Frank's* _____ .
2 _____ .
3 _____ .
4 _____ .
5 _____ .
6 _____ .
7 _____ .

C   **Pronunciation** *-er* endings

4 **11C.1▶** Read and listen to the poem. Underline the words that end in *-er*.

Winter sleep
The days become shorter not longer
The weather becomes colder not warmer
Inside is warmer than outside
His eyes become smaller then close
Sleep the winter sleep
Wait for a better life in the spring

5 Listen again and repeat the poem.

And you? Write two things you have which are:

1 warm   *my coat, my jacket*
2 new   _____
3 expensive   _____
4 old-fashioned _____
5 dirty   _____
6 soft   _____
7 cheap   _____
8 comfortable   _____
9 modern   _____

How well can you compare things now?
Go back to the Student's Book >> p.111 and tick ✓ the line again.

How to **understand opinions**

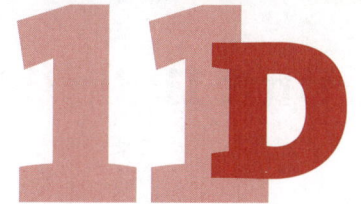

G superlatives **v** furniture; adjectives **P** /w/ /v/ /b/ /p/

A **Vocabulary** furniture; adjectives

1 Match the furniture and the rooms. Some words match more than one room.

sofa   chair   dining table   desk   coffee table
~~bed~~   table   shelf

1 bedroom   *bed* _____
2 living room   _____
3 kitchen   _____
4 office   _____

2 Write more furniture words for each room. Use your dictionary.

3 ~~Cross out~~ the wrong adjective.

1 This is a very comfortable / expensive / ~~fast~~ sofa.
2 His car is the most modern / happiest / most old-fashioned in our street.
3 Your brother is the biggest / oldest / lowest student in the class!
4 Brian's desk is the strongest / fastest / most modern in the office.
5 Which is the most exciting / most relaxing / most useful bar in town?
6 That's the best / strongest / worst newspaper I know.
7 Which train is the most modern / fastest / softest?
8 In summer, Biarritz is the most useful / most expensive / most attractive place on the coast.
9 In many countries, the bus is the cheapest / most useful / strongest kind of transport.

B **Grammar** superlatives

4 Write the superlative form of the adjectives.

1 cheap   *the cheapest* _____
2 long   _____
3 short   _____
4 modern   _____
5 old-fashioned _____
6 hot   _____
7 cool   _____
8 high   _____
9 low   _____
10 expensive   _____

5 Write superlative sentences. Use the adjectives from exercise 4.

1   *A is the cheapest.* _____   *C is the most expensive.* _____

2 _____

3 _____

4 _____

5 _____

C **Pronunciation** /w/ /v/ /b/ /p/

6 Complete the phrases with *w*, *v*, *b*, or *p*.

1 a *b*ottle of *w*ine
2 a _late of _eans
3 a _iece of _a_er
4 a _onderful _iew
5 a _hite _athroom _ash _asin
6 we ha_e _ink, white, or _lack shel_es

7 Check the audio script on » p.94.

8 11D.1▶ Listen and repeat.

How well can you understand and give opinions now?
Go back to the Student's Book » p.113 and tick ✓ the line again.

11 Unit 11 Skills Practice

A Read and understand travel tips

1 Read about travelling in India. Match the headings with the paragraphs.

People   Clothes   Accommodation   Transport   Food

2 Match the highlighted words with the definitions.

1 not cheap but not too expensive _____
2 the money you can spend on your holiday *budget*_____
3 a plant we use to make clothes _____
4 to keep you safe _____
5 a kind of meat _____
6 before the date you want to travel _____

3 Check the information. Write *true* or *false*.

1 It's difficult to buy food when you travel by train. *False*_____
2 In India you need to drive on the left. _____
3 There are no youth hostels in India. _____
4 It's a good idea to wear nylon clothes. _____
5 There's excellent vegetarian food in India. _____
6 People in the north often eat with their hands. _____
7 It's safe to drink all kinds of water. _____
8 English is the main language in India. _____

Visit... India

1 _____

The question is: do you have a big budget or a small budget?
By air: flights are available between the major cities in India.
By train: trains are the most popular transport for long distances. They're cheap but always very busy. Buy your ticket four or five days in advance. Don't worry about food – people sell food at all the stations.
By bus: cheap but always crowded.
By bicycle: cheap and healthy, but don't forget that in India people drive on the left!

2 _____

You can find everything from five-star hotels in the big cities and tourist attractions to small family-run hotels at reasonable prices. Youth hostels are also cheap, clean, and friendly. In smaller towns, it's a good idea to see the room before you decide.

3 _____

Cotton is good for the high temperatures, but nylon can be very uncomfortable. If you're visiting the mountains in the north, take warm clothes. Remember: the higher you travel, the cooler the temperature at night. For your feet, take sandals for the hotter areas and the coast, and boots for the mountains. A hat or cap to protect your head is also a good idea.

4 _____

Indian cooking is one of the wonders of the world! In the south, there are delicious vegetarian dishes with rice or potatoes. Remember that people in the south often eat with their hands. You find meat dishes more often in the north. Don't forget the lamb dishes and cold yogurt drinks. One other important thing: it is safest to drink bottled water.

5 _____

Everyone outside of the big cities is friendly if you try to communicate with them. Language can be a problem – there are 17 main languages – but you can usually find someone who speaks English.

B Read a catalogue

4 Write these words in your language. Use your dictionary.

light

pump

repair kit

brakes

wheel

chain   gears   pedal

5 Look at the information and answer the questions.

a RACING BIKE
► weight 14 kg
► 16 gears
► Pump, repair kit, and lights not included

€250

b TOURING BIKE
► weight 20 kg
► 12 gears
► Pump and lights included

€200

c MOUNTAIN BIKE
► weight 16 kg
► 24 gears
► aluminium frame
► Pump, repair kit, and lights not included

€350

1 Which bike has space for bags? *b*
2 Which is the most expensive? _____
3 Which is the lightest? _____
4 Which one has the most gears? _____
5 Which one includes a pump in the price? _____
6 Which one do you prefer? _____

C Listen for detail

6 Match the words and pictures. Use your dictionary if necessary.

a 1   b   c
d   e   f   g

1 ☐ fridge	4 ☐ microwave	6 ☐ kitchen
2 ☐ heating	5 ☐ toilet paper	7 ☐ towels
3 ☐ pillows		

7 **11S.1▶** Listen to a man talking about a problem. Tick ✓ the words you hear in exercise 6.

8 Listen again and choose the best answer.
1 The angry man is in:
   a his car   b a hotel   c an apartment
2 The man says he has _____ problems.
   a four   b five   c six
3 The reason for the problem is:
   a the man   b the telephone   c the receptionist

9 Match the objects and the problems.
1 ☐ fridge	a there aren't enough
2 ☐ kitchen	b there isn't any
3 ☐ toilet paper	c it doesn't work
4 ☐ heating	d it's dirty
5 ☐ towels	e it's too hot

10 Listen again and complete the sentences.
1 My family and I are in apartment number six, and
   _we___ _____ _____ _____.
2 Just a moment please. Could you _____ _____
   _____ slowly?
3 Now, could you just give _____ _____ _____ ?
4 And what time _____ _____ _____ at the apartment?
5 And what's the _____ _____ _____ apartment?

11 Check the audio script on >> p.94.

D Write about your home

12 Complete the text with these phrases.

a lot of noise   from the living room
from the shops   ~~a quiet part of town~~

We live in a flat in ¹ *a quiet part of town*. It's
five minutes' walk from the park and ten minutes
²_____. There isn't much traffic,
and there aren't too many neighbours, so there isn't
³_____. We live on the fourth floor,
and we can see the river ⁴_____.

at the other end   the biggest room
one of the walls   opposite the TV

My favourite room is the living room. It's
⁵_____ in the flat and it's where we
spend most of our time. There's a comfortable sofa on
one side, ⁶_____ and the bookshelves.
At one end there's a dining table and chairs, and
⁷_____ a glass door that opens on to
the balcony. There's a coffee table in the middle, and
there are lots of photographs on ⁸_____.
I love looking at the photographs and remembering the
people and places.

13 Write about your home. First, describe the location of your home, and second, your favourite room.

*I live ...*_____
_____
_____
_____
_____

*My favourite room is ...*_____
_____
_____
_____
_____

14 Check your writing for mistakes. Show your writing to another student and read his or hers. How can you make yours better?

Now try the Self check on >> p.86.

How to make an appointment

v signs; times of the day **p** intonation to ask and confirm

A Vocabulary signs

1 Complete the crossword.

Across

4 6 7 10 9

Down

1 2

3 5 8

2 Complete the sentences with words from exercise 1.

1 If I don't know the price, I ask the _shopkeeper_ .

2 If I need an eye test, I go to the _____.

3 When I need some extra money, I talk to the
_____.

4 If I get toothache, I go to see the _____.

5 When my dog isn't well, I take him to see the
_____.

6 When my hair's too long, I visit the _____.

7 If the car doesn't work, I make an appointment
with the _____.

8 If my son has a problem at school, I talk to his
_____.

B Vocabulary times of the day

3 Look at Emma's diary. Answer the questions with these
expressions.

tomorrow night mid-morning tomorrow
first thing tomorrow morning early tomorrow evening
late tomorrow morning ~~mid-afternoon tomorrow~~
the day after tomorrow

MON	TUES	WED
	8.30 cleaning lady	
TODAY	10.30 doctor	
	11.30 bank	11.30 shopping
	15.00 mechanic	
	19.00 hairdresser	
	21.30 theatre	

1 When does Emma's car go to the mechanic?
Mid-afternoon tomorrow .

2 When does the cleaning lady arrive?
_____.

3 When is her appointment with the doctor?
_____.

4 When is her appointment with the bank manager?
_____.

5 When does she go shopping? _____.

6 When is her appointment with the hairdresser?
_____.

7 When does she go to the theatre? _____.

C Pronunciation intonation to ask and confirm

4 **12A.1▶** Listen and write A (ask) or C (confirm).

1 ☑C The dentist's 6 ☐ Nine-thirty
2 ☑A The dentist's 7 ☐ An hour later
3 ☐ On Friday morning 8 ☐ An hour later
4 ☐ On Friday morning 9 ☐ For coffee
5 ☐ Nine-thirty 10 ☐ For coffee

5 Check the audio script on ≫ p.94.

6 Listen again and copy the pronunciation.

How well can you make an appointment now?
Go back to the Student's Book ≫ p.117 and tick ✓ the line again.

How to say how you feel

v the body; health   P short and long vowels

A Vocabulary the body

1 Complete the instructions.

1 Put your two h*ands* on your h*ead*.
2 Put your right h_____ on your st_____, and your left h_____ on your b_____.
3 Put your h_____ between your l_____, and your h_____ on your f_____.
4 Put your right f_____ on your h_____, and your left a_____ round your n_____.
5 Put your two h_____ on your b_____.
6 Put your two f_____ round your n_____, and your h_____ on your st_____.
 – and count to 100!

B Vocabulary phrases to say how you feel

2 Match the problems.

1 [*c*][ ][ ] I feel   a it's a headache
2 [ ] I don't feel   b back pains
3 [ ][ ] I think   c ~~terrible~~
4 [ ][ ] I've got   d well
                                e really ill
                                f a stomach ache
                                g awful
                                h it's flu

3 Match the suggestions.

1 [*b*][ ][ ] Don't   a a day off
2 [ ][ ] Stay   b ~~get up~~
3 [ ][ ] Take   c some medicine
                               d go out
                               e at home
                               f in bed
                               g go to work

4 Complete the conversation with these words.

headache   don't   fine   housework   much   ache
with   ~~wrong~~

A Hello! What's [1] *wrong*_____ with you?
B I've got a stomach [2]_____. I think I ate too [3]_____ last night.
A Hmm. Why [4]_____ you take some medicine?
B I don't like medicine!
A Yes, but this is very good! Take it [5]_____ a glass of water. ... Is that better?
B Hey, yes! I feel [6]_____ now!
A That's great! You can get up and do the [7]_____.
B Oh no! I think I'm getting a [8]_____.

C Pronunciation short and long vowels

5 Say these words aloud and write them in the correct box.

~~hat~~   ~~heart~~   cat   hand   arm   back   car   start
half   park

Short vowel sound /æ/	Long vowel sound /ɑː/
hat	heart

~~leg~~   ~~stay~~   friend   pain   head   twelve   they
game   weather   eight

Short vowel sound /e/	Long vowel sound /eɪ/
leg	stay

6 Check your answers in your dictionary. Practise saying the words.

How to talk about future arrangements

G present continuous future   P sentence stress in questions

A Grammar present continuous future

1 Write the verbs in the continuous form.

1 do	*doing*	6 play	_____
2 prepare	_____	7 put	_____
3 go	_____	8 come	_____
4 have	_____	9 take	_____
5 cook	_____	10 help	_____

2 Complete the conversations with the correct form of *be* + a verb from exercise 1.

Satomi So what ¹ *are* you *doing* this weekend, Jim?

Jim Oh, lots of things! My weekend starts early – ²I'____ _____ at a children's party this afternoon.

S Oh yeah?

J Yeah, it's my niece's birthday, and I promised I would go. But ³I'____ _____ dinner for friends this evening, so I have to go to the shops later. What about you?

S Me? Oh, ⁴I'____ _____ away for the weekend. We want to visit Wales. ⁵We'____ _____ the six o'clock train to Cardiff.

J Really? I hope you have a good time!

Mark Are you busy tomorrow, Ana?

Ana Er, yeah. ⁶I'____ _____ tennis mid-morning, and then in the afternoon my friend ⁷____ _____ to stay for a few days. What are you doing?

M ⁸We'____ _____ a party on Saturday night, and wanted to know if you'd like to come.

A Great! I'd love to! Do you need any help?

M Well, ⁹we'____ _____ most of the furniture in another room so there's enough space to dance. ¹⁰We'____ _____ everything mid-afternoon, so if you can come about that time, that would be great. You can bring your friend too!

A OK. Why don't you give me the address?

3 Ivan and Marina are on holiday in Bali. Complete the sentences.

Activities programme

Monday
Go shopping in Ubud, the artists' village
Drive to Lake Batur

Tuesday
Have lunch at Singaraja
Visit the water temple at Bedugul

Wednesday
Buy gifts at the market in Denpasar
Have dinner at Kuta Beach
Watch dance performance at Sanur

1 On Monday they *are going shopping* in Ubud.
2 After that they _____ to Lake Batur.
3 On Tuesday they _____ at Singaraja.
4 After lunch they _____ the temple at Bedugul.
5 On Wednesday they _____ in Denpasar.
6 In the evening they _____ at Kuta Beach.
7 At night they _____ a dance at Sanur.

B Pronunciation sentence stress in questions

4 **12C.1▶** Listen and copy the stress.

1 **What** are you **doing** next **week**?
Where are you **going**?
Who are you **meeting**?
What are you **eating**?

2 **When** are you **go**ing on **hol**iday?
Where are you **stay**ing?
What are you **doing**?
Who are you **tak**ing?

And you? Answer the questions in exercise 4.

1 _____
_____
_____
2 _____
_____
_____
_____

How well can you talk about future arrangements now?
Go back to the Student's Book >> p.121 and tick ✓ the line again.

How to **talk about intentions**

G *going to* for future intentions   **V** lifestyle   **P** fast speech

A Grammar *going to* for future intentions

1 Complete the questions and answers using *going to*.

1 What _are you going to be_ (be) when you grow up?
I _____ (not / be) a doctor.
I _____ (be) a footballer!

2 Where _____ (go) on holiday?
We _____ (visit) the north of Germany.
We _____ (not / stay) in the south.

3 What _____ (do) with the car?
He _____ (drive), so
he _____ (not / drink).

4 What _____ (study) at university?
I _____ (think) about it for a while.
I _____ (not / decide) until next year.

2 Read Cathy's notes. Write *I* for intention, or *A* for arrangement.

1 Phone Helen
_I_

2 meet John at the airport, Fri 9 p.m.
_A_

3 go shopping with Mum Thursday morning
____

4 take children to dentist for their appointments
____

5 have parents' meeting at school Fri 4.30
____

6 work in the garden
____

7 go to Paula's wedding
– Sat 11.30 a.m.
____

8 Sit down and relax!
____

3 Write complete sentences for the notes. Use *going to* or present continuous.

1 *She's going to phone Helen* .
2 *She's meeting John at the airport on Friday* .
3 _____ .
4 _____ .
5 _____ .
6 _____ .
7 _____ .
8 _____ .

B Vocabulary lifestyle

4 Match 1–8 with a–h.

1 ☐d quit   a weight
2 ☐ get   b chess
3 ☐ do   c a gym
4 ☐ lose   d ~~smoking~~
5 ☐ join   e fit
6 ☐ play   f some exercise
7 ☐ eat   g green tea
8 ☐ drink   h healthy food

C Pronunciation understand fast speech

5 **12D.1▶** Listen and write *F* (fast) or *N* (normal).

1 ☐N She doesn't want to go.
2 ☐F She doesn't want to go.
3 ☐ He's going to stop smoking.
4 ☐ He's going to stop smoking.
5 ☐ I want to leave early today.
6 ☐ I want to leave early today.
7 ☐ They aren't going to listen to you!
8 ☐ They aren't going to listen to you!

6 Check the audio script on ≫ p.94. Practise saying the fast sentences.

And you? What are you going to do to be healthier and happier?

1 stop doing?   _I'm going to stop ..._
2 start doing?   _____
3 eat?   _____
4 drink?   _____
5 learn?   _____
6 play?   _____

Unit 12 Skills Practice

A Listen for detail

1 **12S.1▶** Listen to four people making appointments. Complete the table.

	Place	Day	Time
1	bank		
2			
3			
4			

2 Match the questions with the conversations.
a ☐ When would you like the appointment?
b ☐ That's Friday, isn't it?
c ☐ 1 Did you say Tuesday?
d ☐ What's the problem?
e ☐ Eleven o'clock?
f ☐ Is that the bank?
g ☐ Did you say seven o'clock?
h ☐ Twelve o'clock on Monday?

3 Listen to the first conversation again. Put the words in order.

1 I'd like to make an _____.
   manager speak the to please to appointment

2 One moment please. OK, _____?
   which were day thinking you of

3 Some time _____.
   week this the weekend before

4 Right, thank you Mr Brunel. That's next _____

   _____.
   eleven Thursday in at morning the

4 Check the audio script on ›› p.94.

B Read for detail

5 Read the notes and complete Mark's diary.

Hi, Helen!

Sorry, Monday night I'm studying – I've got an exam first thing the next morning. Are you going to Satomi's party on Tuesday night? Maybe see you there.

Mark

****

Hi Mark,

We're going out for a drink on Monday night. Do you want to come with us?

Helen

Baybridge Dental Clinic

34 Kenwood Drive, Chester
Tel. 0725 339-4168

Your next appointment:

Tuesday 27th April, 12.00 p.m.

Mark!
Don't forget –
it's your turn to
clean the kitchen
and bathroom on
Wed morning!

John

Mark
You weren't here
when I called.
Are you still OK
for lunch on Wed
at Blake's – and the
cinema at 8.30?
Call me! Paula

Mark,
Remember you're going to help me
choose your father's present on
Monday! See you at the Main St. exit in
the shopping centre at 1.30.

Love, Mum

Chester Amateur Football Club

NEXT MATCH:
Tues 27th, 4 p.m.

(Meet at the park 3.30)

---

26 Monday	27 Tuesday	28 Wednesday
9-12 classes	Morning _____	Morning _____
1.30 _____	12.00 _____	1.00 _____
night _____	3.30 _____	8.30 _____
	4.00 _____	
	night _____	

C Read adverts

6 Write these words in the adverts.

garage   hairdresser's   optician's   supermarket

a

The country's favourite

Special offers every day!
Look for the prices in red.

**FRESH FOOD AT
FABULOUS PRICES.**

Order by phone or on the Internet
Open Mon–Sat 9 a.m.–9 p.m.
Sundays 11 a.m.–5 p.m.
Car park 200 spaces
Tel. 685-2219

www.gateways.net

b

Waves 'n' Curls

Welcome to your local

– for men and women.

**This week's special offer:
one FREE child's haircut
for every adult customer.**

By appointment only

Open
Mon–Sat 9 a.m.–6 p.m.
Tel 685-4395

(Closed Wednesdays)

c

Insight

If you can't read these
adverts, we can help!!

*All kinds of glasses
and contact lenses.
The best selection in town.
Reading glasses from only £10.
Come and see us!*

Open Mon–Fri 9.30–5.30

45 South St.
(opposite the post office)

d

MORRISONS

✓ **We repair all kinds of car.**
✓ **Fast and reliable service.**

FREE OIL CHANGE
WHEN YOU MAKE
AN APPOINTMENT.

Call for an appointment now:
Tel. 685-7791

67 Bute St. (next to cinema)

7 Answer the questions.

1 Which place closes on Wednesdays? _b_
2 Which two places have special offers? ____ and ____
3 What time does the optician's close? ____
4 Which place has its own website? ____
5 What do I get if I make an appointment at the garage? ____
6 Where can I order by phone? ____
7 How much do reading glasses cost? ____
8 Which place is nearest to the cinema? ____

8 <u>Underline</u> three words you don't know. Guess their meanings, and check in your dictionary.

D Write a letter

9 Read the wedding invitation. Complete Maika's reply with these words.

company   happy   ~~invitation~~   love   say
show   wonderful

Linda Spencer and David Taylor
would like you to
come to their wedding
on Saturday 28 July 2007
at two o'clock
at St. Mary's Church
Lemon Tree Walk
Oxford
and afterwards at the Welcome Hotel, Oxford

Dear Linda,

Thank you very much for the ¹ _invitation_ to your
wedding. I was very ² _____ to hear your
news. I would ³ _____ to go to the wedding,
but my ⁴ _____ is sending me to
South America for a week, and I really can't
⁵ _____ no! Maybe you can ⁶ _____
me the wedding photographs when I come back.
I hope you have a ⁷ _____ day!
Best wishes,
Maika

10 Imagine you get this invitation to a party, but you can't go. Write your own letter.

Please come to Satomi's birthday party.

Place: 25 Barnton Road
Date: Friday 27th September
Time: 10 p.m.

Bring a bottle!

Dear Satomi,
_____
_____
_____
_____
_____

11 Check your writing for mistakes.

Now try the Self check on » p.87.

Unit 1 Self check

1

Grammar

1 Complete the text with these words.

I'm   name's   is   my   my   number's   is

My ¹_____ John Evans. ²_____ from York in England. England
³_____ in Britain, in Europe. I'm British. I speak English. ⁴_____
address ⁵_____ 18 Park Street. ⁶_____ phone ⁷_____ 837 7382.

2 Underline the correct word.
1 What is / are your name?
2 Where are you / your from?
3 What's / What your address?
4 How / What old are you?
5 What is you / your email address?

Vocabulary

3 Write the numbers.

1	11	_eleven_	5	19	_____
2	3	_____	6	55	_____
3	17	_____	7	76	_____
4	8	_____	8	12	_____

4 Order the words to make sentences and questions.
1 name   your   what's   me   excuse
_____ ?
2 jim@teleline.uk   address   his   is   email
_____ .
3 for   thanks   coffee   the
_____ .
4 it   spell   you   how   do
_____ ?
5 phone   my   is   91 456 2110   number
_____ .

Pronunciation

5 Write the letters with the same sound in the correct box.

~~j~~   v   i   l   k   b   n   f   d

a	m	t	y
_j_	_____	_____	_____
_____	_____	_____	_____

Check your answers on >> p.88.

What are you going to do now?
a Nothing. I'm happy.
b Revise grammar / vocabulary / pronunciation and try again.
c Ask another student / my teacher for help.

To revise go to ...
Student's Book Review >> p.15   Grammar Bank >> p.136
Workbook >> pp.4–7   **www.oup.com/elt/result**

Reading

Read these texts again.
Workbook >> p.8 exercise 1
Workbook >> p.9 exercise 9

How confident are you?
I can understand ...
☐ some words
☐ with help
☐ when I read again
☐ everything

Listening

Listen to this audio again.
Workbook >> p.8 audio script **1S.1▶**

How confident are you?
I can understand ...
☐ some words
☐ with help
☐ when I listen again
☐ everything

Writing

Do this writing exercise again.
Workbook >> p.9 exercise 11

How confident are you?
I can write ...
☐ with help
☐ on my own
☐ with some mistakes
☐ with no mistakes

What are you going to do now?
a Nothing. I'm happy.
b Ask my teacher for help.
c Practise my reading / listening / writing.

To practise go to ...
Student's Book >> pp.6–14
Workbook >> pp.8–9
MultiRom Listening section
www.oup.com/elt/result

76   Self checks

Unit 2 Self check

Grammar

1 Add *'s* to complete the text.

Hi! My name Max. I'm from Canada. I'm eighteen years old and I live with my parents. My mother name Sara and she a doctor. My father name Jed and he a driver.

2 Complete the sentences with these possessives.

our my their his her your

1 Kemal's parents live in Turkey. _____ house is in Izmir.
2 John's brother is a singer. _____ name is Steve.
3 We live in London. _____ address is 12 Eaton Street.
4 Thomas, what is _____ mother's name?
5 Rita is from Spain but _____ husband is English.
6 I'm from Ireland. _____ name's Michael.

Vocabulary

3 Complete the sentences with these words.

married rich old single young divorced

1 Their daughter is very _____. She's three.
2 My brother is _____. His wife's name is Eleanor.
3 David is _____. He has a big apartment in New York.
4 He's an _____ man. He's seventy-five.
5 He is not her husband now. They are _____.
6 My sister's 25 and she's not married, she's _____.

4 Complete the phrases with the correct word.

1 10.30   h_____ past ten
2 11.15   q_____ past eleven
3 5.50   t_____ to six
4 6.40   t_____ to seven
5 12.00 a.m. m_____

Pronunciation

5 Say the words aloud. <u>Underline</u> the stressed syllable.

Example <u>twen</u>ty

1 thirty   5 nineteen
2 fifty   6 seventeen
3 sixteen   7 forty
4 ninety   8 fourteen

Check your answers on >> p.88.

What are you going to do now?

a Nothing. I'm happy.
b Revise grammar / vocabulary / pronunciation and try again.
c Ask another student / my teacher for help.

To revise go to ...
Student's Book Review >> p.25   Grammar Bank >> p.137
Workbook >> pp.10–13   **www.oup.com/elt/result**

Reading

Read this text again.
> **Workbook** >> p.14 exercise 8

How confident are you?
I can understand ...

- [ ] some words
- [ ] with help
- [ ] when I read again
- [ ] everything

Listening

Listen to this audio again.
> **Workbook** >> p.14 audio script **2S.1▶**
> **Workbook** >> p.14 audio script **2S.2▶**

How confident are you?
I can understand ...

- [ ] some words
- [ ] with help
- [ ] when I listen again
- [ ] everything

Writing

Do this writing exercise again.
> **Workbook** >> p.15 exercise 13

How confident are you?
I can write ...

- [ ] with help
- [ ] on my own
- [ ] with some mistakes
- [ ] with no mistakes

What are you going to do now?

a Nothing. I'm happy.
b Ask my teacher for help.
c Practise my reading / listening / writing.

To practise go to ...
Student's Book >> pp.16–24
Workbook >> pp.14–15
MultiRom Listening section
www.oup.com/elt/result

Unit 3 Self check

Grammar

1 Complete the text with the correct form of the verbs in brackets.

I ¹_____ (be) from Turkey. The capital of Turkey ²_____ (be) Ankara but I ³_____ (live) in Trabzon. Our currency ⁴_____ (be) the Turkish lira. My first language ⁵_____ (be) Turkish but I ⁶_____ (speak) German very well.

2 Complete the text with *a*, *an*, or *the*.

I'm Polish and I live in Poland. ¹_____ capital city is Warsaw but I live in ²_____ town called Nowe Miasto. It's near Warsaw. In Poland ³_____ currency is ⁴_____ złoty. ⁵_____ main language is Polish but I speak Russian very well too. I also speak ⁶_____ little English and ⁷_____ little French.

Vocabulary

3 Complete the sentences.
1 The language and nationality of the people from Turkey is _____.
2 The _____ of Russia is Moscow.
3 The nationality of the people from China is _____.
4 The _____ of Germany is the euro.
5 Washington is the capital of _____ USA.

4 Correct the spelling mistakes.
1 I speak Portugese.
2 I speak France and a little German.
3 I'm Brasilian and I live in São Paulo.
4 The nationality of the people from Peru is Peruian.
5 Berlin is the capitel of Germany.

Pronunciation

5 Read the texts aloud. Put the underlined words in the correct box.

●•	●
toilets	

A Excuse me, where are the <u>toilets</u>, please?
B They're over there near <u>platform</u> 12.

A Excuse me, where's the <u>pub</u>, please?
B It's upstairs, near the <u>chemist's</u>.

A Excuse me, where are the <u>taxis</u>, please?
B Taxis? They're near the Fairfield Street <u>exit</u>.

A Excuse me, is this the <u>train</u> to London?
B Sorry, I don't know.

Check your answers on >> p.88.

What are you going to do now?
a Nothing. I'm happy.
b Revise grammar / vocabulary / pronunciation and try again.
c Ask another student / my teacher for help.

To revise go to ...
Student's Book Review >> p.35   Grammar Bank >> p.138
Workbook >> pp.16–19 **www.oup.com/elt/result**

Reading

Read these texts again.
Workbook >> p.20 exercise 6
Workbook >> p.21 exercise 7

How confident are you?
I can understand ...
☐ some words
☐ with help
☐ when I read again
☐ everything

Listening

Listen to this audio again.
Workbook >> p.20 audio script **3S.1▶**

How confident are you?
I can understand ...
☐ some words
☐ with help
☐ when I listen again
☐ everything

Writing

Do this writing exercise again.
Workbook >> p.21 exercise 12

How confident are you?
I can write ...
☐ with help
☐ on my own
☐ with some mistakes
☐ with no mistakes

What are you going to do now?
a Nothing. I'm happy.
b Ask my teacher for help.
c Practise my reading / listening / writing.

To practise go to ...
Student's Book >> pp.26–34
Workbook >> pp.20–21
MultiRom Listening section
www.oup.com/elt/result

Unit 4 Self check

Grammar

1 Tick ✓ or correct the sentences.

1 He doesn't works at weekends.
2 Does you work in a bank?
3 She doesn't go for a run.
4 She gets dressed and brush her teeth.
5 He finishs work at five.
6 Does she works at weekends?

2 Correct the underlined words.

In Ethiopia we usually get up ¹in six o'clock in the morning and go to bed ²on nine or ten o'clock ³of the evening. We have our main meal ⁴on about half past twelve. We often have a small meal ⁵in six o'clock ⁶at the evening.

Vocabulary

3 Complete the sentences with a suitable word.

1 We u_ _ _ _ _ _ _ work nine to five here.
2 You a_ _ _ _ _ _ arrive late.
3 But I n_ _ _ _ _ leave late!
4 How o_ _ _ _ do you have coffee breaks?
5 You s_ _ _ _ _ _ _ _ _ _ leave at twelve o'clock and come back at two!

4 Complete the sentences with these words.

vacancies   out   closed   cancelled   order   private

1 I'm at the airport but my flight's _____!
2 I want to buy a ticket from the machine but it's out of _____.
3 I want to stay at the Royal Hotel but there are no _____.
4 You can't go to the supermarket. It is _____ on Sundays.
5 Everyone wants to go to the game. The tickets are sold _____.
6 The sign outside his house says '_____. No entry'.

Pronunciation

5 Say these words aloud and write them in the correct box.

~~live~~ ~~leave~~ sit fifth eat free beach chip thing see

/iː/	/ɪ/
leave	live
_____	_____
_____	_____
_____	_____
_____	_____

Check your answers on >> p.88.

What are you going to do now?

a Nothing. I'm happy.
b Revise grammar / vocabulary / pronunciation and try again.
c Ask another student / my teacher for help.

To revise go to ...
Student's Book Review >> p.45   Grammar Bank >> p.139
Workbook >> pp.22–25   www.oup.com/elt/result

Reading

Read these texts again.
   Workbook >> p.26 exercise 1
   Workbook >> p.27 exercise 7

How confident are you?
I can understand ...
☐ some words
☐ with help
☐ when I read again
☐ everything

Listening

Listen to this audio again.
   Workbook >> p.26 audio script **4S.1▶**

How confident are you?
I can understand ...
☐ some words
☐ with help
☐ when I listen again
☐ everything

Writing

Do this writing exercise again.
   Workbook >> p.27 exercise 10

How confident are you?
I can write ...
☐ with help
☐ on my own
☐ with some mistakes
☐ with no mistakes

What are you going to do now?

a Nothing. I'm happy.
b Ask my teacher for help.
c Practise my reading / listening / writing.

To practise go to ...
Student's Book >> pp.36–44
Workbook >> pp.26–27
MultiRom Listening section
www.oup.com/elt/result

Unit 5 Self check

Grammar

1 <u>Underline</u> the correct words.
1 Does / Has he got brown hair?
2 Anne doesn't / hasn't got a dog.
3 Has / Have you got a pen?
4 I haven't / don't have got any paper.
5 You has / have got a problem.

2 Read the conversation and <u>underline</u> the best words.
A I need a gift for my friend Jane.
B Does she [1]likes / got / like wine?
A No, she [2]don't / not like / doesn't.
B Has she got a DVD player?
A No, she [3]haven't / hasn't got / hasn't.
B OK, give [4]she / her / him a DVD player.
A They're very expensive.
B Oh, OK. Does she like animals?
A Yes, she [5]do / does / has.

Vocabulary

3 Match 1–5 with a–e.
1 ☐ Do you know my girlfriend Kate?
2 ☐ My name's Al. It's
3 ☐ Steven, this
4 ☐ Sorry, what's your
5 ☐ Hi Walter. Do

a is Richard.
b name again?
c you remember me?
d Come and meet her.
e short for Alan.

4 Order the words to make sentences and questions.
1 has small eyes grey she .
2 Eric got cat big black has a .
3 an car old red he drives .
4 blonde woman know you the tall do ?
5 got hair dark Frank has long .

Pronunciation

5 Write the words in the correct box.

comp<u>le</u>te wr<u>i</u>te <u>e</u>vening <del>hate</del> n<u>o</u>te ph<u>o</u>ne <u>u</u>se
pl<u>a</u>ce st<u>u</u>dent w<u>i</u>ne

/eɪ/	/iː/	/aɪ/	/əʊ/	/juː/
hate	_____	_____	_____	_____
_____	_____	_____	_____	_____

Check your answers on ≫ p.88.

What are you going to do now?
a Nothing. I'm happy.
b Revise grammar / vocabulary / pronunciation and try again.
c Ask another student / my teacher for help.

To revise go to ...
Student's Book Review ≫ p.55   **Grammar Bank** ≫ p.140
Workbook ≫ pp.28–31   **www.oup.com/elt/result**

Reading

Read these texts again.
Workbook ≫ p.32 exercise 1
Workbook ≫ p.33 exercise 7

How confident are you?
I can understand ...
☐ some words
☐ with help
☐ when I read again
☐ everything

Listening

Listen to this audio again.
Workbook ≫ p.32 audio script **5S.1**▶

How confident are you?
I can understand ...
☐ some words
☐ with help
☐ when I listen again
☐ everything

Writing

Do this writing exercise again.
Workbook ≫ p.33 exercise 11

How confident are you?
I can write ...
☐ with help
☐ on my own
☐ with some mistakes
☐ with no mistakes

What are you going to do now?
a Nothing. I'm happy.
b Ask my teacher for help.
c Practise my reading / listening / writing.

To practise go to ...
Student's Book ≫ pp.46–54
Workbook ≫ pp.32–33
MultiRom Listening section
www.oup.com/elt/result

Unit 6 Self check

Grammar

1 <u>Underline</u> the correct words.

Iris Oh dear, I haven't got many tea bags. Have you got ¹any / much?

Sue Yes. How ²much / many do you need?

Iris Two. No, nine or ten ... some for later! ... This is your milk, is that OK? I haven't got ³some / any.

Sue OK. Help yourself!

Iris Oh, there isn't much ... Oops, there isn't any for you, sorry! ... How ⁴much / many sugar do you want? I don't take sugar in tea. Do you?

Sue Well, ehm ...

Iris No, of course you don't. I'd like a biscuit. Have you got ⁵a / any?

Sue Yes, I've got ⁶a / some lot of biscuits, but they're ...

Iris Oh great. Thanks! ... These biscuits are delicious!

2 Write the words in the correct box.

~~egg~~ computer cup coffee CD milk sugar mobile biscuit cheese jam onion bread steak meat

Countable	egg
Uncountable	

Vocabulary

3 Complete these sentences with the correct word.

1 For b_____, a lot of people go to the bars to drink orange juice or coffee with milk, and eat small cakes.

2 They don't drink much t_____, and they never drink it with milk.

3 Don't go for l_____ before two o'clock – you can't get the 'menu of the day' before that.

4 The first c_____ is soup, salad or vegetables.

5 The evening m_____ is at nine or ten o'clock.

4 Correct the spelling mistakes.

1 Are there any potatos in a Russian salad?

2 Are there any carots?

3 I would like a cheese sandwiche.

4 We need appels and bananas.

5 Would you like a biscit with your coffee?

Pronunciation

5 <u>Underline</u> the /ə/ sound.

yog<u>u</u>rt potato supermarket tomato salad sugar

Check your answers on >> p.89.

What are you going to do now?

a Nothing. I'm happy.

b Revise grammar / vocabulary / pronunciation and try again.

c Ask another student / my teacher for help.

To revise go to ...
Student's Book Review >> p.65   Grammar Bank >> p.141
Workbook >> pp.34–37   **www.oup.com/elt/result**

Reading

Read this text again.

> **Workbook** >> p.38 exercise 2

How confident are you?

I can understand ...

- [ ] some words
- [ ] with help
- [ ] when I read again
- [ ] everything

Listening

Listen to this audio again.

> **Workbook** >> p.39 audio script **6S.1▶**

How confident are you?

I can understand ...

- [ ] some words
- [ ] with help
- [ ] when I listen again
- [ ] everything

Writing

Do this writing exercise again.

> **Workbook** >> p.39 exercise 10

How confident are you?

I can write ...

- [ ] with help
- [ ] on my own
- [ ] with some mistakes
- [ ] with no mistakes

What are you going to do now?

a Nothing. I'm happy.

b Ask my teacher for help.

c Practise my reading / listening / writing.

To practise go to ...
Student's Book >> pp.56–64
Workbook >> pp.38–39
MultiRom Listening section
www.oup.com/elt/result

Unit 7 Self check

Grammar

1 Tick ✓ or correct the sentences.
  1 My problem is I can't swimming.
  2 Do you go for a run in the morning?
  3 What time do you having lunch?
  4 I enjoy watch football on TV.
  5 She can to swim very quickly.
  6 Tom can do it easy.
  7 Gary likes having long hair.

2 Underline the correct words.
  1 What shall / are we do?
  2 Let's / Let go out.
  3 Shall / How about going to the cinema?
  4 How about / Let's going to the shops?
  5 Let's ask / asking William to come to the party.

Vocabulary

3 Complete the sentences with the correct form of *go* or *play*.
  1 I always _____ fishing on Sunday morning.
  2 Do you enjoy _____ cards?
  3 Let's _____ roller-skating this afternoon.
  4 Every summer they _____ sailing in the Mediterranean.
  5 I love _____ basketball!
  6 I want to _____ the guitar.

4 Complete the sentences with these words.

  windy   wet   snowy   icy   dry   cloudy

  1 The weather is very hot and _____. My flowers need water.
  2 It's very _____ today – perfect for skiing!
  3 Be careful if you go roller-skating. The roads are very _____.
  4 It's very _____ in England – it rains all the time.
  5 It's not a good day for golf because it's very _____.
  6 You can't see the sun today because it's very _____.

Pronunciation

5 Underline the stressed syllable in each word.

  average   photograph
  exercise   director
  gardening   typical
  piano   newspaper

Check your answers on >> p.89.

What are you going to do now?
  a Nothing. I'm happy.
  b Revise grammar / vocabulary / pronunciation and try again.
  c Ask another student / my teacher for help.

To revise go to …
Student's Book Review >> p.75   Grammar Bank >> p.142
Workbook >> pp.40–43   www.oup.com/elt/result

Reading

Read these texts again.
  Workbook >> p.44 exercise 4
  Workbook >> p.45 exercise 6

How confident are you?
I can understand …
  ☐ some words
  ☐ with help
  ☐ when I read again
  ☐ everything

Listening

Listen to this audio again.
  Workbook >> p.44 audio script **7S.1▶**

How confident are you?
I can understand …
  ☐ some words
  ☐ with help
  ☐ when I listen again
  ☐ everything

Writing

Do this writing exercise again.
  Workbook >> p.45 exercise 10

How confident are you?
I can write …
  ☐ with help
  ☐ on my own
  ☐ with some mistakes
  ☐ with no mistakes

What are you going to do now?
  a Nothing. I'm happy.
  b Ask my teacher for help.
  c Practise my reading / listening / writing.

To practise go to …
Student's Book >> pp.66–74
Workbook >> pp.44–45
MultiRom Listening section
www.oup.com/elt/result

Unit 8 Self check

Grammar

1 <u>Underline</u> the best words.

Gene Hackman is Harry Caul, a spy. He ¹watching / watches people. He ²is listening / listens to their conversations and makes tapes. He ³isn't understanding / doesn't understand the conversations – they aren't his problem.

One day, Harry is listening to a conversation. The people ⁴are talking / talk about a murder plan. This is a problem for Harry. He doesn't like murders. But Harry ⁵is making / making a mistake. He thinks he is listening to other people, but really *they* ⁶are listening / listen to *him*.

2 Order the words to make sentences and questions.

1 the wearing is girl jeans blue ?
2 skirts friends wearing are girl's the ?
3 the musicians are jackets wearing ?
4 dictionary I'm using a not .
5 aren't they sandals their wearing .

Vocabulary

3 Match 1–5 with a–e.

1 ☐ I'm wearing sandals,   a a suit and tie.
2 ☐ We're going to a wedding   b or a skirt.
3 ☐ At work I wear   c a warm coat and a hat.
4 ☐ I could wear a dress   d so don't wear trainers.
5 ☐ It's very cold. Wear   e not boots.

4 Complete the sentences with these words.

to on for to about

1 John's listening _____ the radio.
2 We need to think _____ the grammar.
3 Can you sit _____ that chair?
4 I'm going _____ a walk.
5 We're going _____ the gym this afternoon.

Pronunciation

5 Put these words in the correct box.

~~board~~ bird short shirt fur walk work four

/ɔː/	/ɜː/
board	_____
_____	_____
_____	_____

Check your answers on >> p.89.

What are you going to do now?

a Nothing. I'm happy.
b Revise grammar / vocabulary / pronunciation and try again.
c Ask another student / my teacher for help.

To revise go to ...
Student's Book Review >> p.85   Grammar Bank >> p.143
Workbook >> pp.46–49   www.oup.com/elt/result

Reading

Read these texts again.
   Workbook >> p.50 exercise 1
   Workbook >> p.51 exercise 7

How confident are you?
I can understand ...
   ☐ some words
   ☐ with help
   ☐ when I read again
   ☐ everything

Listening

Listen to this audio again.
   Workbook >> p.50 audio script **8S.1▶**

How confident are you?
I can understand ...
   ☐ some words
   ☐ with help
   ☐ when I listen again
   ☐ everything

Writing

Do this writing exercise again.
   Workbook >> p.51 exercise 11

How confident are you?
I can write ...
   ☐ with help
   ☐ on my own
   ☐ with some mistakes
   ☐ with no mistakes

What are you going to do now?

a Nothing. I'm happy.
b Ask my teacher for help.
c Practise my reading / listening / writing.

To practise go to ...
Student's Book >> pp.76–84
Workbook >> pp.50–51
MultiRom Listening section
www.oup.com/elt/result

Grammar

1 Complete the text with the verbs in brackets in the past simple.

I ¹_____ (walk) up the hill to the Nightmare Hotel. I ²_____ (stop) at the door but I ³_____ (can not) see the bell. I ⁴_____ (knock) and I ⁵_____ (wait) in the cold and windy night. I ⁶_____ (look) in the window but there ⁷_____ (not be) any light.

2 Correct the underlined words.
1 I <u>haved</u> a sandwich for lunch yesterday.
2 The weather <u>were</u> terrible last night.
3 They <u>do</u> the homework last night.
4 He <u>telled</u> me an interesting story.
5 We <u>go</u> to Warsaw last year.

Vocabulary

3 Complete these phrases with the correct word for giving directions.
1 Don't go right, go l_____ at the corner.
2 The bank is o_____ the museum.
3 Walk a_____ the road.
4 Go out o_____ the door and into the street.
5 The post office is n_____ to the museum.

4 Underline the correct words.
A What was the weather like?
B Perfect. It was warm and ¹sunny / clean.
A Where did you stay? A hotel?
B Yeah, a small hotel. Nice and ²quiet / noisy, with a beautiful garden and a ³lovely / boring view of the beach and the countryside.
A Was the beach nice?
B Yeah, ⁴delicious / beautiful, yeah. And it wasn't ⁵crowded / dry.

Pronunciation

5 Put the words in the correct box.

~~asked~~ closed ended looked knocked started stopped waited

1-syllable verb ●	2-syllable verb ● ●
asked	_____
_____	_____
_____	_____

Check your answers on >> p.89.

What are you going to do now?
  a Nothing. I'm happy.
  b Revise grammar / vocabulary / pronunciation and try again.
  c Ask another student / my teacher for help.

To revise go to ...
Student's Book Review >> p.95   Grammar Bank >> p.144
Workbook >> pp.52–55   **www.oup.com/elt/result**

Reading

Read these texts again.
  Workbook >> p.56 exercise 2
  Workbook >> p.57 exercise 8

How confident are you?
I can understand ...
  ☐ some words
  ☐ with help
  ☐ when I read again
  ☐ everything

Listening

Listen to this audio again.
  Workbook >> p.56 audio script **9S.1▶**

How confident are you?
I can understand ...
  ☐ some words
  ☐ with help
  ☐ when I listen again
  ☐ everything

Writing

Do this writing exercise again.
  Workbook >> p.57 exercise 13

How confident are you?
I can write ...
  ☐ with help
  ☐ on my own
  ☐ with some mistakes
  ☐ with no mistakes

What are you going to do now?
  a Nothing. I'm happy.
  b Ask my teacher for help.
  c Practise my reading / listening / writing.

To practise go to ...
Student's Book >> pp.86–94
Workbook >> pp.56–57
MultiRom Listening section
www.oup.com/elt/result

Unit 10 Self check

Grammar

1 Underline the correct words.
1 Did you go / went out last Friday?
2 Did / Were you work on Saturday?
3 Ernie didn't have / had a son.
4 Ernie get / got married when he was forty.
5 We didn't / weren't sell the car.

2 Write past simple questions about Pablo Neruda.
1 Where / Pablo Neruda / born
_____ ?
2 What / real name
_____ ?
3 Where / go to live
_____ ?
4 When / write his first poem
_____ ?
5 When / win the Nobel Prize for Literature
_____ ?

Vocabulary

3 Match 1–5 with a–e.
1 ☐ I got married
2 ☐ I became a doctor
3 ☐ He went to university
4 ☐ She left school in 2001
5 ☐ He became a diplomat

a and studied German.
b and went to university.
c and had a child.
d and worked in many countries.
e and got a job in a hospital.

4 Write the years.

1800 *eighteen hundred*

1919 _____   1999 _____
1984 _____   2012 _____
2008 _____   1933 _____

Pronunciation

5 Do the underlined letters make a /s/ or a /z/ sound? Write the words in the correct box.

~~news~~ facts his place studies was this quiz

/s/	_____ _____ _____
/z/	*news* _____ _____ _____ _____

Check your answers on >> p.89.

What are you going to do now?
a Nothing. I'm happy.
b Revise grammar / vocabulary / pronunciation and try again.
c Ask another student / my teacher for help.

To revise go to ...
Student's Book Review >> p.105   Grammar Bank >> p.145
Workbook >> pp.58–61   www.oup.com/elt/result

Reading

Read these texts again.
> **Workbook** >> p.62 exercise 1
> **Workbook** >> p.63 exercise 8

How confident are you?
I can understand ...
☐ some words
☐ with help
☐ when I read again
☐ everything

Listening

Listen to this audio again.
> **Workbook** >> p.62 audio script **10S.1▶**

How confident are you?
I can understand ...
☐ some words
☐ with help
☐ when I listen again
☐ everything

Writing

Do this writing exercise again.
> **Workbook** >> p.63 exercise 14

How confident are you?
I can write ...
☐ with help
☐ on my own
☐ with some mistakes
☐ with no mistakes

What are you going to do now?
a Nothing. I'm happy.
b Ask my teacher for help.
c Practise my reading / listening / writing.

To practise go to ...
Student's Book >> pp.96–104
Workbook >> pp.62–63
MultiRom Listening section
www.oup.com/elt/result

Unit 11 Self check

Grammar

1 Write *enough* in each sentence below.

1 The water isn't warm for swimming.
2 He is 1 m 80. The bed isn't big for him.
3 I'm not rich to live in central London!
4 There aren't chairs in the TV room.
5 Oh no! I don't have cups for everyone!

2 Underline the correct words.

1 Ricky's bed is longest / longer than Frank's.
2 The chair is more expensive / expensive than the sofa.
3 This holiday is worse / badder than our holiday last year.
4 That desk is the ugliest / uglier in the shop.
5 What is the warmest / most warm country in Europe?

Vocabulary

3 Match 1–5 with a–e.

1 ☐ You stay for the night and only have breakfast
2 ☐ You have a flat and you cook and clean
3 ☐ You sleep outside
4 ☐ A campsite is a place
5 ☐ The five-star hotel has

a in a tent.
b in a self-catering apartment.
c where people put their tents.
d a bar, pool, and restaurants.
e in a bed and breakfast.

4 Complete the sentences with these words.

lift   washbasin   hand-made   antique   shelf

1 I need a _____ for my books.
2 There is a small _____ in the bathroom.
3 This _____ table is two hundred years old.
4 The chairs were _____ by my father. He loved making things.
5 We have to walk up the stairs because the _____ is broken.

Pronunciation

5 Underline the stressed syllable in each word.

attractive   fantastic   friendly
comfortable   beautiful   modern
excellent   delicious   ugly

Check your answers on >> p.90.

What are you going to do now?

a Nothing. I'm happy.
b Revise grammar / vocabulary / pronunciation and try again.
c Ask another student / my teacher for help.

To revise go to ...
Student's Book Review >> p.115   Grammar Bank >> p.146
Workbook >> pp.64–67   www.oup.com/elt/result

Reading

Read this text again.
Workbook >> p.68 exercise 1

How confident are you?
I can understand ...
☐ some words
☐ with help
☐ when I read again
☐ everything

Listening

Listen to this audio again.
Workbook >> p.69 audio script 11S.1▶

How confident are you?
I can understand ...
☐ some words
☐ with help
☐ when I listen again
☐ everything

Writing

Do this writing exercise again.
Workbook >> p.69 exercise 13

How confident are you?
I can write ...
☐ with help
☐ on my own
☐ with some mistakes
☐ with no mistakes

What are you going to do now?

a Nothing. I'm happy.
b Ask my teacher for help.
c Practise my reading / listening / writing.

To practise go to ...
Student's Book >> pp.106–114
Workbook >> pp.68–69
MultiRom Listening section
www.oup.com/elt/result

Unit 12 Self check

Grammar

1 Write the complete questions. Use the present continuous.

1. When / Justin / take a day off sick?
2. What / you / do on Friday?
3. How / you / get there?
4. Where / you / stay?
5. Where / you / go this evening?
6. Who / you / see tonight?

2 Order the words to make sentences.

1. at two sister meeting my o'clock I'm .
2. I'm Tony tennis tonight playing with .
3. next learn going German I'm to year .
4. quit to I'm smoking going .
5. Ana tomorrow lunch with I'm having .

Vocabulary

3 Complete the sentences with these words.

weekdays afternoon thing day evening

1. His appointment is late tomorrow _____, at 5.30.
2. The appointment is at 10.45 the _____ after tomorrow.
3. I'm going to the bank first _____ tomorrow. At 8 a.m.
4. We're meeting in a café at 8.00 this _____.
5. She starts work at 9.00 on _____ and 10.00 at weekends.

4 Underline the correct words.

1. I don't feel good / well.
2. I think I'm / it's flu.
3. I'm going to phone in ill / sick.
4. He's going to take / make a day off work.
5. Mary's not in the office because she's on sick leave / holiday.

Pronunciation

5 Match the words with the sounds.

1. ☐ feel   a /æ/
2. ☐ fill   b /e/
3. ☐ fun   c /əʊ/
4. ☐ hat   d /ɑː/
5. ☐ heart   e /eɪ/
6. ☐ not   f /iː/
7. ☐ note   g /ɪ/
8. ☐ pain   h /ʌ/
9. ☐ pen   i /ɒ/

Check your answers on >> p.90.

What are you going to do now?

a Nothing. I'm happy.
b Revise grammar / vocabulary / pronunciation and try again.
c Ask another student / my teacher for help.

To revise go to ...
Student's Book Review >> p.125   **Grammar Bank** >> p.147
Workbook >> pp.70–73   **www.oup.com/elt/result**

Reading

Read these texts again.
Workbook >> p.74 exercise 5
Workbook >> p.75 exercise 6

How confident are you?
I can understand ...
☐ some words
☐ with help
☐ when I read again
☐ everything

Listening

Listen to this audio again.
Workbook >> p.74 audio script **12S.1▶**

How confident are you?
I can understand ...
☐ some words
☐ with help
☐ when I listen again
☐ everything

Writing

Do this writing exercise again.
Workbook >> p.75 exercise 10

How confident are you?
I can write ...
☐ with help
☐ on my own
☐ with some mistakes
☐ with no mistakes

What are you going to do now?

a Nothing. I'm happy.
b Ask my teacher for help.
c Practise my reading / listening / writing.

To practise go to ...
Student's Book >> pp.116–124
Workbook >> pp.74–75
MultiRom Listening section
www.oup.com/elt/result

Self checks answer key

Unit 1

Grammar
1
1 name's
2 I'm
3 is
4 My
5 is
6 My
7 number's

2
1 is
2 you
3 What's
4 How
5 your

Vocabulary
3
1 eleven
2 three
3 seventeen
4 eight
5 nineteen
6 fifty-five
7 seventy-six
8 twelve

4
1 Excuse me, what's your name?
2 His email address is jim@teleline.uk.
3 Thanks for the coffee.
4 How do you spell it?
5 My phone number is 91 456 2110.

Pronunciation
5 a, j, k
m, f, l, n
t, v, b, d
y, i

Unit 2

Grammar
1 Hi! My name's Max. I'm from Canada. I'm eighteen years old and I live with my parents. My mother's name's Sara and she's a doctor. My father's name's Jed and he's a driver.

2
1 Their
2 His
3 Our
4 your
5 her
6 My

Vocabulary
3
1 young
2 married
3 rich
4 old
5 divorced
6 single

4
1 half
2 quarter
3 ten
4 twenty
5 midnight

Pronunciation
5
1 thirty
2 fifty
3 sixteen
4 ninety
5 nineteen
6 seventeen
7 forty
8 fourteen

Unit 3

Grammar
1
1 am/'m
2 is/'s
3 live
4 is/'s
5 is
6 speak

2
1 The
2 a
3 the
4 the
5 The
6 a
7 a

Vocabulary
3
1 Turkish
2 capital
3 Chinese
4 currency
5 the

4
1 I speak **Portuguese**.
2 I speak **French** and a little German.
3 I'm **Brazilian** and I live in São Paulo.
4 The nationality of the people from Peru is **Peruvian**.
5 Berlin is the **capital** of Germany.

Pronunciation
5 ●● toilets, platform, chemist's, taxis, exit
● pub, train

Unit 4

Grammar
1
1 He doesn't work at weekends.
2 Do you work in a bank?
3 ✓
4 She gets dressed and brushes her teeth.
5 He finishes work at five.
6 Does she work at weekends?

2
1 at
2 at
3 in
4 at
5 at
6 in

Vocabulary
3
1 usually
2 always
3 never
4 often
5 sometimes

4
1 cancelled
2 order
3 vacancies
4 closed
5 out
6 Private

Pronunciation
5 /iː/ leave, eat, free, beach, see
/ɪ/ live, sit, fifth, chip, thing

Unit 5

Grammar
1
1 Has
2 hasn't
3 Have
4 haven't
5 have

2
1 like
2 doesn't
3 hasn't
4 her
5 does

Vocabulary
3
1 d
2 e
3 a
4 b
5 c

4
1 She has small grey eyes.
2 Eric has got a big black cat.
3 He drives an old red car.
4 Do you know the tall blonde woman?
5 Frank has got long dark hair.

Pronunciation

5 /eɪ/ hate, place
/iː/ complete, evening
/aɪ/ write, wine
/əʊ/ note, phone
/juː/ use, student

Unit 6

Grammar

1 1 any
2 many
3 any
4 much
5 any
6 a

2 Countable: egg, computer, cup, CD, mobile, biscuit, onion, steak
Uncountable: coffee, milk, sugar, cheese, jam, bread, meat

Vocabulary

3 1 breakfast
2 tea
3 lunch
4 course
5 meal

4 1 Are there any **potatoes** in a Russian salad?
2 Are there any **carrots**?
3 I would like a cheese **sandwich**.
4 We need **apples** and bananas.
5 Would you like a **biscuit** with your coffee?

Pronunciation

5 yog<u>u</u>rt
p<u>o</u>tato
s<u>u</u>permarket
t<u>o</u>mato
sal<u>a</u>d
sug<u>a</u>r

Unit 7

Grammar

1 1 My problem is I can't swim.
2 ✓
3 What time do you have lunch?
4 I enjoy watching football on TV.
5 She can swim very quickly.
6 Tom can do it easily.
7 ✓

2 1 shall
2 Let's
3 How about
4 How about
5 ask

Vocabulary

3 1 go
2 playing
3 go
4 go
5 playing
6 play

4 1 dry
2 snowy
3 icy
4 wet
5 windy
6 cloudy

Pronunciation

5 <u>a</u>verage
<u>e</u>xercise
<u>ga</u>rdening
<u>pia</u>no
<u>pho</u>tograph
director
<u>ty</u>pical
<u>new</u>spaper

Unit 8

Grammar

1 1 watches
2 listens
3 doesn't understand
4 are talking
5 is making
6 are listening

2 1 Is the girl wearing blue jeans?
2 Are the girl's friends wearing skirts?
3 Are the musicians wearing jackets?
4 I'm not using a dictionary.
5 They aren't wearing their sandals.

Vocabulary

3 1 e
2 d
3 a
4 b
5 c

4 1 to
2 about
3 on
4 for
5 to

Pronunciation

5 /ɔː/ board, short, walk, four
/ɜː/ bird, shirt, fur, work

Unit 9

Grammar

1 1 walked
2 stopped
3 couldn't
4 knocked
5 waited
6 looked
7 wasn't

2 1 had
2 was
3 did
4 told
5 went

Vocabulary

3 1 left
2 opposite
3 across
4 of
5 next

4 1 sunny
2 quiet
3 lovely
4 beautiful
5 crowded

Pronunciation

5 ● asked, closed, looked, knocked, stopped
●● ended, started, waited

Unit 10

Grammar

1 1 go
2 Did
3 have
4 got
5 didn't

2 1 Where was Pablo Neruda born?
2 What was his real name?
3 Where did he go to live?
4 When did he write his first poem?
5 When did he win the Nobel Prize for Literature?

Vocabulary

3 1 c
2 e
3 a
4 b
5 d

Self checks answer key

4 1919 nineteen nineteen
1984 nineteen eighty-four
2008 two thousand and eight
1999 nineteen ninety-nine
2012 two thousand and twelve
1933 nineteen thirty-three

Pronunciation
5 /s/ fac**ts**, pla**ce**, thi**s**
/z/ new**s**, hi**s**, studie**s**, wa**s**, qui**z**

Unit 11
Grammar
1 1 The water isn't warm enough for swimming.
2 He is 1 m 80. The bed isn't big enough for him.
3 I'm not rich enough to live in central London!
4 There aren't enough chairs in the TV room.
5 Oh no! I don't have enough cups for everyone!

2 1 longer
2 more expensive
3 worse
4 ugliest
5 warmest

Vocabulary
3 1 e
2 b
3 a
4 c
5 d

4 1 shelf
2 washbasin
3 antique
4 hand-made
5 lift

Pronunciation
5 at**tr**active
comfortable
ex**c**ellent
fan**t**astic
beau**t**iful
de**li**cious
friendly
modern
ugly

Unit 12
Grammar
1 1 When is Justin taking a day off sick?
2 What are you doing on Friday?
3 How are you getting there?
4 Where are you staying?
5 Where are you going this evening?
6 Who are you seeing tonight?

2 1 I'm meeting my sister at two o'clock.
2 I'm playing tennis with Tony tonight.
3 I'm going to learn German next year.
4 I'm going to quit smoking.
5 I'm having lunch with Ana tomorrow.

Vocabulary
3 1 afternoon
2 day
3 thing
4 evening
5 weekdays

4 1 well
2 it's
3 sick
4 take
5 leave

Pronunciation
5 1 f
2 g
3 h
4 a
5 d
6 i
7 c
8 e
9 b

Audio scripts

1

1A.1

A Hel**lo**, good **mor**ning! **What's** your **name**?
B Hel**lo**, good **mor**ning! **My** name's **Jane**.
A **Nice** to **meet** you! **My** name's **Drew**.
B Hel**lo**. **Drew**. **Nice** to meet **you**!

1B.1

Phone numbers
384 6652
499 7411
406 5889
221 3075

Email addresses
iou20@busby.net
okchen@vanzine.int
quick4@spt.com
lin3@lovebird.org

Websites
www.boptunes.esl
www.ugetwell.co.uk
www.digipix.net
www.readit.net

1C.1

What's your **first** name? Claire.
What's your **sur**name? Palmer.
How do you **spell** that? P-A-L-M-E-R.
Where are you **from**? Canada.
What's your ad**dress**? 42 Ashford Street, Toronto.

1S.1

1 **A** Good morning, sir. Your name please?
 B Marwan Raharjo.
 A **How do you spell your surname?**
 B R-A, H-A-R, J-O.
 A R-A, H-A-R, J-O. Thank you. And your age?
 B I'm thirty-five.
 A Forty-five?
 B No, thirty-five.
 A And where are you from?
 B Holland.
 A H-O, double L, A-N-D. Thank you. And your email? Do you have an email address?
 B Yes, it's, er, marwara@belanda.net. That's M-A-R, W-A-R-A at B-E-L, A-N-D-A.
 A B-E-L, A-N-D-A.
 B Yes, that's right. Dot net.
 A Dot net. Right! Thank you, sir.

2 **A** Good evening! Miss van der Post?
 B Yes?
 A This is hotel reception speaking. I'm sorry, but I can't read your writing on the form. Could I just check your details?
 B Yes, of course.
 A Thank you. Could you tell me your first name?

 B Gillian.
 A Erm, is that with a J or a G?
 B With a G. G-I, double L, I-A-N.
 A G-I, double L, I-A-N. And your marital status?
 B **Sorry?**
 A Are you married?
 B Oh no, no I'm not. I'm single.
 A **Two more questions.** What's your phone number?
 B 976 343 918.
 A 9-7-6, 3-4, 3-9, 1-8. And your passport number?
 B My passport number. Just a moment. Ah yes: SA – 500255.
 A SA – 5 double 0, 2 double 5. Thank you very much.
 B You're welcome.

3 **A** Now, Mr Collins, **four more questions, please.** What's your first name?
 B Sean.
 A **Could you spell that for me?**
 B S-E-A-N.
 A S-E-A-N. OK. Age?
 B **Can you just repeat that?**
 A Your age. How old are you?
 B Ah! I'm 31.
 A Thirty-one. And your marital status?
 B Married.
 A Right – married. And question number four – what's your passport number?
 B I don't remember. You have my passport!
 A Oh yes, you're right – here it is! Erm, it's er RI-2273168. RI, double 2 7, 3-1, 6-8. Thank you.

2

2A.1

2-syllable words: question, Monday, Wednesday, answer, evening, English, weekend, Thursday

3-syllable words: afternoon, underline, umbrella, Saturday

2C.1

His girlfriend is an English teacher.
Her parents are designers.
She's an engineer.
The shop assistant is sixteen years old.
My boyfriend is a good actor.

2D.1

1 It's half past six.
2 It's quarter to ten.
3 It's two thirty.
4 It's ten to eight.
5 It's twenty past four.
6 It's about five o'clock, um, yes, five to five.

2D.2

Is it on TV1? No, it's on TV2.
Is it on Monday morning?
No, it's on Monday **evening**.
Is it on Tuesday morning?
No, it's on **Monday** morning.
Is it at six o'clock?
No, it's at **twelve** o'clock.
Is it at ten past eight?
No, it's at **twenty** past eight.
Is it at five to nine?
No, it's at five to **ten**.
Is it the news?
No, it's the **football**.

2S.1

1 This is a recorded message. Doctor Watson's office **is closed at** the moment. The doctor is available on Tuesday **and Thursday evenings**, from six o'clock to nine o'clock. That's Tuesday and Thursday evenings from six to nine.

2 Hello. Sorry, but we are now closed. The office is open from Tuesday to Friday, in the mornings, between half-past nine and half-past two. That's Tuesday to Friday, 9.30 to 2.30. Thank you.

3 This is a recorded message. Thank you for calling. Please call again in shop opening times. The shop is open every day Monday to Saturday, nine o'clock to half-past four in the afternoon. Thank you.

4 This is Bristol Street Primary School. Sorry, but the school is closed at the moment. Please call later. The school is open every day, Monday to Friday, from 8.30 in the morning to 4.30 in the afternoon. That's 8.30 to 4.30. Thank you.

2S.2

1 Hi, my name's Eric. I'm from France. I'm **25 years old**, and I'm single. I live with my parents. And my job? Well, **I'm a designer**.

2 This is my girlfriend, Maria. No, **not my wife** – my girlfriend! She's 23, she's from Italy, and she's **a shop assistant**.

3 These two are my friends from university. They're **a married couple**. Their names are Annie and Paul. They have no children. He's an engineer, a computer engineer, and she's a school teacher, a **primary school teacher**.

4 This is Françoise. She's 37 and **she's divorced**. She has two children: a young boy of six and a girl of sixteen. **She isn't rich**. She's an office worker.

5 **These are friends** who live in Switzerland. His name is Klaus and her name is Louise. **They aren't married**. She's 22 years old and a university student. He's about 30, and he's a doctor at the local hospital.

3

3A.1

Is this the train to Manchester?
No, that train's on platform 4.

Excuse me! Where are the telephones?
They're over there, near the exit.

Where's the café, please?
It's upstairs, near the music shop.

Excuse me, is this the car park?
No, it isn't. It's over there, near the chemist's.

Excuse me, where are the cash machines, please?
They're near the bookshop.

3B.1

Portugal
Portuguese
Egypt
Egyptian
Japan
Japanese
China
Chinese

3C.1

house houses
school schools
watch watches
shop shops
church churches
glass glasses
street streets
girl girls
town towns

3S.1

A Excuse me. **Is there a bus stop near here**?
B A bus stop? Yes, madam. It's just outside.
A Can you show me on the map?
B Yes, of course. A5, that's it there.
A A5?
B That's right.
A Thank you very much.

A Sorry?
B Yes?
A I need some cash, and I can't find any cash machines.
B Oh. Well, er, **look, the cash machines are there**, erm, A14.
A Oh I see. A14. Thanks!

A Excuse me.
B Yes?
A I can't see the map properly, and **I don't have my glasses with me**. Could you tell me where the toilets are?

B The toilets? Erm, that's them right there – A8.
A Eighty-eight?
B No, A – 8, near the supermarket.
A Oh, sorry! A8. Thank you very much.

A Excuse me! I'm looking for the South Street exit.
B Oh yes. That's, er, A2, **at the other end of the shopping centre**. Near the toilets.
A A2? Thanks.

A Sorry?
B Yes?
A Do you know if there's a chemist's here?
B Erm, just a moment. Let's have a look at the map. Chemist's. **Oh yes, here it is**! A7, next to the bookshop.
A A7, next to the bookshop. Thanks!

4

4A.1
The football's on in five minutes but the TV is out of order. – Oh no!

I'm at the supermarket and everything is half-price today. – That's great!

My car! My car! It's not in the car park! – Oh no!

We have a new car! – Oh really?

My sister has a new baby. – That's great!

We get married on Monday! – Good luck!

My father's in bed. – Oh really?

My cat isn't very well. – I'm sorry!

School is closed today. – That's great!

It's 9.30 and my exam's at ten o'clock. – Good luck!

4B.1
1 the seventh of April
2 the fifteenth of April
3 the fourth of August
4 the twentieth of August
5 the third of October
6 the ninth of October

4C.1
He wakes up early.
She gets up late.
He checks the mail.

She goes for a run.
He has fruit for breakfast.
She leaves the house.

He watches TV.
She brushes her teeth.
He finishes work.

4S.1
A So, Jack, you're a lorry driver. Tell me **about your** normal week.
J Normal week? **I don't have** any normal weeks! Yeah, well, I usually work **Monday to Friday**, but, erm, it's often **weekends** too. I mean, for example, I live in France, you know, and, er, on Monday I drive to Holland for a container, and I take, take that to Germany.
A And how long is the trip?
J About a day, I suppose, yeah, a day or so. Anyway, so I'm in Holland on Monday, then, er, I sleep in Germany on Tuesday night, you know, and then on Wednesday, er, I go from Germany to the north of Italy.
A So when do you arrive in Italy?
J If I'm lucky, I get there on Wednesday night, but it all depends, you know, the traffic, the weather ...
A Yeah, right. And after Italy?
J Well, usually I go up to Austria, you know. That's quite near, so I can relax on Thursday, maybe go for a run in the evening.
A Ah, so you have, er, like a break on Thursdays?
J Yeah, usually. Not always, you know! Sometimes I have to go to another country.
A And Fridays? What do you do on Fridays?
J Well, on Fridays the usual thing is to come back to France, and maybe do a small local job.
A You mean you arrive in France on Friday?
J Normally, yes.
A So your family – what about the family? Do you see them often?
J Maybe on Saturdays and Sundays, when I'm at home in France. But sometimes I'm away from home for two or three weeks, so I don't see them very often.
A So do you like driving your lorry?
J Well! It's not easy. The hours are long and the money isn't so good. It's just a job ...

5

5D.1
I've **got** a **bike** but I **haven't got** a **car**.
I've **got** a **clock** but I **want** to get a **watch**.
I've **got** a **cat** but I'd **rather** have a **dog**.
I've **got** a **flat** but I **want** to buy a **house**.
I've **got** a **wife** but she **isn't** very **nice**.
Sorry, dear.

5S.1
a A Mr Patel! **How** are you?
  B Fine, thanks, Mike. And you?
  A **We're** fine, thank you. Do you know my brother Henry?
  B No, I don't think so.
  A Come and meet **him**. Henry, this is Mr Patel, **our** neighbour. Mr Patel, Henry, my **brother**.
  C Nice to meet you!
  B Yes, **you** too.

b A Hello Jenny! Do you remember me?
  B Erm, sorry, no, I don't.
  A Oh Jenny! My name's Ricardo!
  B Ricardo ... Just a moment – are you Ricky Marvin?
  A Yes, that's right! Ricky Marvin, from school.
  B Oh yes, I remember you now. Long blond hair, blue eyes. You've got short hair now, and it's brown.
  A Yes. Oh, and this is my wife, Elena.
  B Nice to meet you, Elena!

c A Who's that woman over there?
  B Where?
  A Over there, next to the window. The woman with long brown hair and green eyes.
  B Ah, that's Sheila. We work together at the office.
  A Oh really?
  B Yes. Come and meet her. Sheila, this is my wife, Stella. Stella, this is Sheila.
  A&C Nice to meet you!
  A Sorry, what's your name again?
  C Sheila.
  A So you work at the office with Bill?
  C Yes, that's right ...

6

6A.1
How **much** are the **crisps**?
How **much** is the **wine**?
They're **one** euro **twen**ty,
and **five** ninety-**nine**.

6C.1
My sister likes an actor,
so she buys him a flower,
she sends him a letter,
but he never sends an answer.

6D.1
some **bread** and **but**ter
some **ham** and **eggs**
a **piece** of **piz**za
some **chicken legs**
some **tea** or **coffee**
with **milk** or **su**gar
What would you **like**?
a **glass** of **wa**ter
– **please**!

6S.1
1 A Is the food all right, madam?
  B Yes, thank you. It's fine.
  A Would you like any wine?
  B Ah, yes, please.
  A Red or white?
  B Red, please.
  A Would you like a bottle or glass?
  B Oh, er, a bottle please. A bottle of red wine.
  A Thank you, madam.

2 A Hello, Jane. Have you got any crisps?
  B Er, yes, I have.

A Oh really? Well, I've got an apple, but I don't like apples.
B So?
A Well, I want some crisps. Can I give you my apple, and you give me the crisps?
B How many do you want?
A How many? Erm, the bag of crisps!
B Oh, OK. Here you are.
A Wow, thanks!
B And my apple?
A Oops, sorry!

3 A Anna! It's lovely to see you.
  B It's good to see you too, John.
  A Would you like a cup of coffee?
  B Yes, please, I'd love one.
  A Do you take milk?
  B No, thanks.
  A Sugar?
  B Er, yes, please.
  A There are some sandwiches on the table. Butter or jam – help yourself!
  B Thank you, that's great.
  A So, tell me your news ...

4 A Oh, hello Bob. How are you?
  B Fine thanks, Jeff. Erm, listen, have you got any eggs?
  A Eggs?
  B Yeah, my girlfriend's here for lunch, and I haven't got any eggs.
  A How many do you want?
  B Four would be great!
  A OK. Anything else?
  B Well, erm, sugar?
  A How much sugar do you need?
  B A cup of sugar would be great, thanks.
  A OK, I won't be a second.
  B Thanks very much!

7

7C.1
She can drive a bus,
she can run fast,
and she can understand Spanish,
but she **can't** cook anything,
she **can't** play football,
and she **can't** remember my name!

7D.1
Hello Henry!
house and home
half an hour
Who works hard?
She hates the housework!
When's your holiday?
I need help with my homework!

7S.1
Welcome to the Holiday Out Club! We are open six months a year and offer activities for all different age groups. I'd just like to take a moment to explain the map of the club for you. Number one on your map is the main hotel building – that's the hotel at number one. And, erm, opposite the hotel is the car park. We have spaces for 200 cars, you

know! So, number eleven is the car park. Now, next to that you can see the, er, cinema at number twelve, and the disco at number ten. **Have you got that?** That's the cinema at number twelve, and disco at number ten. Erm, now, let me see, ah yes, next to the hotel we have the shopping centre, that's, er, restaurants at number two, and bars next door at number four – **all right?** The bars at number four, yes. That means the shops are at number three, and the hairdresser's is at number five. **OK?** That brings us to number six, the gym, next to the shopping centre. That's right! That's the gym, with lots of activities, sports, and exercises for everyone! Opposite the gym is the park, **can you see that?** That's number eight, the park. And then next to the park is the swimming pool. Yes, that's number nine, the swimming pool. Finally, on the right, you can see the River Wyle. That's number seven. We use the river for boating and also for swimming. **Any questions?** No? Well, that's all, thank you. We hope you enjoy your stay with us. If you do have any questions, our staff will be very happy to help you …

8

8A.1
A We usually have a snack at about four o'clock.
B It's ten to four now. Let's eat!

A We're going to the football match.
B Oh! I'd love to go to the match!

A We're going for a sandwich. Would you like one?
B I'd like two please! One ham, one cheese.

A We're going for a drink! Would you like to come?
B I'd love to come, but I've got two exams tomorrow – English and maths.

8B.1
I can't find my shirts!
We're going to work this afternoon.
What's that board on the tree?
She lives on the third floor.
Mum! Where are my football shorts?
What time do you start working?
Smith! Is this your bird?
What's the fourth country on the map?

8C.1
something – anything – nothing
reading – writing – speaking
driving a car
walking in the park
riding a bike
making dinner
doing exercises
having a bath
thinking about you

8D.1
We're watching **them**, but **they** aren't watching **us**.
He's looking at **her**, but **she** isn't looking at **him**.
She likes **him**, but **he** doesn't like **her**.
He always phones **her**, but **she** never phones **him**!
We sometimes invite **them**, but **they** don't invite **us**!
She talks about **him**, but **he** doesn't talk about **her**.

8S.1
A Can you hear me all right?
B Yes. I'm in the station. Describe the man for me.
A OK. He's about sixty years old. Yes, sixty. He's **a tall man**, with grey hair – **short grey hair**. He's holding a magazine. No, not a magazine, sorry, a newspaper.
B OK. What's he wearing?
A Um, he's wearing a coat, **a long black coat**. He's not wearing a suit, but he is wearing a shirt and tie. Yes, that's right, a shirt and tie. Maybe **a black tie**.
B Is he carrying anything?
A Yes, I think he's carrying a sweater over his arm.
B Is he wearing glasses?
A No, he's not.
B Hmm … this is difficult. There are lots of men that look the same. What about his shoes?
A Oh! He's wearing **white shoes**, white shoes, now I remember!
B Aha! There he is!

9

9A.1
1 Excuse me, how can I get to the museum, please?
2 Excuse me, how can I get to the museum, please?
3 Excuse me, how can I get to the airport, please?
4 Excuse me, how can I get to the airport, please?
5 Excuse me, how can I get to the hospital, please?
6 Excuse me, how can I get to the hospital, please?
7 Excuse me, how can I get to the park, please?
8 Excuse me, how can I get to the park, please?

9B.1
It's the first left at the corner.
There's a bank at the corner.
The post office is just opposite.
Go straight on and turn left at the lights.
The map says there's an art gallery near here.
It's across the bridge and on the left.
Turn right again into Union Street.
I think there's a tourist information office in the station.

9C.1
4 The beach is nice
  The boys are fun
  The water is warm
  In the holiday sun
  But my parents are here
  But my parents are here

5 The food was good
  The weather was great
  The drinks were cheap
  The bars opened late
  But our daughter was there
  But our daughter was there

9D.1
He waited at the bus stop.
It started to rain.
He opened his umbrella.
A voice asked him to help.
He answered her question.
They walked into town.
They talked all the way.
And who knows what happened after that!

9S.1
Well, I went to France **last summer**, on a **cheap holiday**. I stayed in youth hostels, you know, where **you can meet** lots of **young people**, and, er, they tell you all the **good places** to visit. I was travelling alone, I mean, I just wanted a break. The first day I got a cheap flight to Lyon and then travelled west into the mountains. Just fantastic! The real countryside of France! Lots of small towns with their castles and traditions. And then, one day in the middle of France, I met a friend of mine from university! It was incredible! I arrived at this youth hostel, and there was Brian, waiting for the place to open! So we talked and talked about friends and work and family – it was just great! And another day I found this amazing ceramics shop in a little village – you know how I love ceramics – and I spent the day watching this woman make her things. Ah, and I was very lucky with the weather. In the whole three weeks I was there, it only rained twice. I can't wait to go back. It was such a wonderful holiday!

10

10A.1
I met my new boss this morning!
What did you think?
They went to a Thai restaurant.
What did they eat?
My brother phoned.
What did he say?
We went shopping yesterday.
What did you buy?
His children were on TV!
What did they do?
My parents are here.
When did they come?
She went away last summer.
Where did she go?
It's not raining now.
When did it stop?

10B.1
He wrote home.
She rides like an adult.
We sent her a gift for her birthday.
That's Batman!
It's a hard job!
They went down this morning.

10C.1
Tommy was a **wai**ter
Who **didn't** like his **boss**
He **didn't** really **hate** her
But he **didn't** keep his **job**

10D.1
Greenpeace
blue eyes
Police!
Yes, Miss
plays in the theatre
these books

10S.1
A Did you see the film on TV last night?
B No, I didn't. I was studying.
A Poor thing!
B I had an exam this morning! Anyway – what happened?
A This woman had a cat, right?
B OK.
A And there was something wrong with the cat, so she took it to the vet's clinic.
B **And?**
A Well, the cat died.
B Oh no!
A Yes, and then the woman wanted revenge on the vet.
B But vets don't kill animals!
A I know, but she thought the vet was bad and didn't help the cat.
B **So what did she do?**
A Well, she sent him a box of chocolates. Poisoned chocolates. But he didn't eat them.
B **Why not?**
A He didn't like chocolates! He gave them to someone else, and that person nearly died.
B **Didn't she stop then?**
A No, no! The vet wasn't dead, so she didn't stop. She sent him a book with poisoned pages.
B Oh, yeah?
A Yeah, but he didn't like the book, so he didn't even open it.
B No luck with the poison, eh?
A No.
B **So did she kill him in the end?**
A Well, she got really angry and went to the vet's clinic with a gun. She waited at the door, and when the vet came out …
B **She shot him?**
A She tried, but the gun didn't work!
B Lucky for the vet!
A Yeah, so in the end, the police took her away.
B Hmm, shame I missed it …

11

11A.1
adjective
conversation
exercise
information
interview
sentences
syllables
vocabulary

11C.1
Winter sleep
The days become shorter not longer
The weather becomes colder not warmer
Inside is warmer than outside
His eyes become smaller then close
Sleep the winter sleep
Wait for a better life in the spring

11D.1
a bottle of wine
a plate of beans
a piece of paper
a wonderful view
a white bathroom washbasin
we have pink, white, or black shelves

11S.1
A Fairfield Holiday Apartments. Can I help you?
B Er, yes! Yes, you can! My family and I are in apartment number six, and **we have a problem**.
A And what's the problem?
B As a matter of fact, there are several problems.
A Oh dear. What's wrong?
B The fridge doesn't work, the kitchen is dirty, there's no toilet paper, the heating is too hot ...
A Erm, just a moment please. Could you **repeat that more** slowly?
B The fridge doesn't work.
A Yes.
B The kitchen is dirty.
A OK.
B There's no toilet paper.
A I see.
B The temperature's too hot. The heating is too high.
A All right. Anything else?
B There aren't enough towels in the bathroom.
A Uh-huh. Now, erm, could you just give **me your name**?
B Jones, Jonathan Jones.
A Right, Mr Jones. And what time **did you arrive** at the apartment?
B Half-past four this afternoon.
A And what's the **number of your** apartment?
B Number 6. I told you that at the beginning!
A Yes, you did. Well, Mr Jones, you do have a problem!
B I know! I told you that as well! Isn't anybody going to do anything?
A Oh yes, Mr Jones! You're in the wrong apartment. Your reservation is for apartment number 16, not number 6! Didn't you come to reception when you arrived?
B What? Reception? Er, well, yes, I'm sure we did – didn't we?

12

12A.1
1 The dentist's.
2 The dentist's?
3 On Friday morning?
4 On Friday morning.
5 Nine-thirty.
6 Nine-thirty?
7 An hour later.
8 An hour later?
9 For coffee?
10 For coffee.

12C.1
What are you doing next week?
Where are you going?
Who are you meeting?
What are you eating?

When are you going on holiday?
Where are you staying?
What are you doing?
Who are you taking?

12D.1
1 She doesn't want to go.
2 She doesn't wanna go.
3 He's gonna stop smoking.
4 He's going to stop smoking.
5 I wanna leave early today.
6 I want to leave early today.
7 They aren't going to listen to you!
8 They aren't gonna listen to you!

12S.1
1 **A** Briggs Bank, King Street branch. Can I help you?
B Is that the bank?
A Yes, sir. This is Briggs Bank.
B Erm, **I'd like to make an appointment to speak to the manager, please**.
A **One moment, please ... OK, which day were you thinking of?**
B Er, **some time this week, before the weekend**.
A Would Thursday be all right?
B Did you say Tuesday?
A No, sorry, Thursday!
B Yes, that's fine.
A At eleven in the morning?
B Eleven o'clock?
A Yes.
B That's fine. My name's Brunel.
A **Right, thank you Mr Brunel. That's next Thursday at eleven in the morning**.
B Thursday at eleven o'clock. Fine. Bye!

2 **A** Baybridge Dentist. Good morning.
B Erm, good morning! Erm, I need to see a dentist.
A Yes. You'd like to make an appointment?
B Please. I've got this terrible toothache!
A I see. When would you like the appointment?
B Oooh, as soon as possible!

A Yes, well, how about seven o'clock this evening?
B Did you say seven o'clock? Is there anything earlier than that?
A Erm, only at 4.15, madam.
B 4.50?
A No, madam – 4.15.
B Ah! All right, er, 4.15 is fine.
A And your name please?
B Johnson, T. Johnson.
A All right, Ms Johnson. We'll expect you today at 4.15.
B Thank you very much!

3 **A** Good afternoon, Wilson's Mechanic's here.
B Ah, yes, erm, I've got a problem with the car.
A Erm, what's the problem?
B I don't know. The car doesn't work. Could you have a look at it?
A You'll need to make an appointment, I'm afraid. Let me see ... I can give you a time for next week.
B Next week?!
A Yes, madam. Today is Thursday.
B All right. How about Monday?
A Monday ... Monday lunch time, erm, twelve o'clock.
B Twelve o'clock on Monday?
A Yes, madam. Can I have your name, please?
B Erm, Weaver, Jenny Weaver.
A Right, thank you Ms Weaver. We'll see you on Monday.
B Thanks. Bye-bye.

4 **A** Unisex Hairdresser. Can I help you?
B Yes, please. I'd like an appointment to get my hair cut.
A One moment, please. Right. When would that be for?
B Have you got anything for tomorrow afternoon?
A I'm sorry, sir. We're all full for tomorrow. I can give you a time for the day after.
B That's Friday, isn't it?
A Yes, that's right.
B OK. So, er, what time then?
A Is six in the afternoon all right?
B Erm, yes, that sounds fine.
A And your name please?
B Oh, sorry, erm, David Taylor.
A Thank you, Mr Taylor. That's Friday 27th at six p.m.
B Thank you! Bye!

Irregular verbs

verb	past simple
be	was
	were
break	broke
buy	bought /bɔːt/
can	could /kʊd/
come	came
cut	cut
do	did
draw	drew
drink	drank
drive	drove
eat	ate
find	found
forget	forgot
get	got
give	gave
go	went
have	had
hear	heard /hɜːd/
know	knew /njuː/
learn	learnt
	learned
leave	left
lose	lost

verb	past simple
make	made
meet	met
put	put /pʊt/
read	read /red/
ring	rang
run	run
say	said /sed/
see	saw /sɔː/
sell	sold
send	sent
sing	sang
sit	sat
sleep	slept
speak	spoke
spend	spent
stand	stood /stʊd/
swim	swam
take	took /tʊk/
tell	told
think	thought /θɔːt/
understand	understood
wake up	woke up
wear	wore
write	wrote

« Look at the verb column.
Cover the past simple column
and test yourself.

OXFORD
UNIVERSITY PRESS

Great Clarendon Street, Oxford OX2 6DP

Oxford University Press is a department of the University of Oxford.
It furthers the University's objective of excellence in research, scholarship,
and education by publishing worldwide in

Oxford New York

Auckland Cape Town Dar es Salaam Hong Kong Karachi
Kuala Lumpur Madrid Melbourne Mexico City Nairobi
New Delhi Shanghai Taipei Toronto

With offices in

Argentina Austria Brazil Chile Czech Republic France Greece
Guatemala Hungary Italy Japan Poland Portugal Singapore
South Korea Switzerland Thailand Turkey Ukraine Vietnam

OXFORD and OXFORD ENGLISH are registered trade marks of
Oxford University Press in the UK and in certain other countries

ISBN: 978 0 19 430486 3

Printed in China

ACKNOWLEDGEMENTS

Illustrations by: Jo Bird/Jelly Illustration pp.55, 67; Emma Brownjohn/New
Division pp.6, 12, 14, 19, 28 top, 33, 36, 40 bottom, 47 left, 50, 53 bottom, 65
right; Clod/Comillus pp.11, 28 left, 29 right, 39, 46, 48 bottom, 54, 60, 64; Bob
Dewar p.23; Mark Duffin pp.4, 16, 18 left, 31, 35, 37, 47 right, 52 right, 56
right, 65 left, 69, 72; Helen Flook p.49; Pamela Goodchild via BL Kearley p.26
top; Glyn Goodwin pp.18 top, 24, 59; Simon Gurr p.57; Matt Johnstone/Jelly
Illustration pp.17, 26 bottom, 44, 56 left; George Onions pp.40 top, 71; Gavin
Reece pp.5, 25, 48 top; Mark Ruffle pp.10, 29 left, 34, 41 right, 53 top, 61, 62,
70; Phillip Warner p.43

*The Publishers and Author would also like to thank the following for permission to
reproduce photographs*: AKG p.51 (Paramount/Black Rain/Rear Window);
Anthony Blake Photolibrary pp.36 (Tim Hill/Risotto), 39 (Tim Hill/rice/risotto);
Corbis Images pp.15 (REUTERS/Ethan Mille/Sade), 45 (C. Lyttle/zefa/man and
grapes); Dawes p.68 (bicycles); DK Images p.36 (Spaghetti Bolognese, Russian
Salad); Empics pp.15 (Manu Fernandez/Ronaldinho, Claude Haller/Anastacia),
63 (Gurinder Osan); Getty Images pp.4 (Altrendo images/shaking hands), 21
(Lars Klove/hotel at night, Ryan McVay/hotel sitting room), 45 (PicturePress/
woman and dogs), 47 (Ken Weingart/couple with boy, Matthias Clamer/couple
with girl); iStockphoto p.22 (Velden/no vacancies sign); Ronald Grant Archive
p51 (Galaxie/Greenwich/Diva); Sally and Richard Greenhill pp.14 (c), 72 (Mark),
74 (Mark); Kobal Collection p.51 (UGC/Studio Canal/*Amelie*); Mercedes Benz
p.66; National Museum of Art, Architecture and Design, Oslo p.62; Oxford
University Press pp.4 (portraits), 7 (couple), 11, 12, 14 (a, b, d, e), 31, 36 (pasta,
meat, tomatoes, onion, cheese, potatoes, egg, yogurt, fish, peas, chicken,
rice, onion, carrots, salt), 42 (Bob, Lucy), 68 (Taj Mahal); Punchstock p.21
(bedroom); Rex Features pp.7 (Coldplay), 9, 15 (Ben Stiller, Stella McCartney),
20, 51 (*Snakes on a Plane*), 66 (old car); Zyro p.68 (bicycle accessories)

Recordings produced by: Leon Chambers